HIGHER
ALGEBRA

for the Undergraduate

HIGHER ALGEBRA

ALGEBRA

for the Undergraduate

THE LATE MARIE J. WEISS
Professor of Mathematics
Newcomb College
Tulane University

NEW YORK · JOHN WILEY & SONS, INC.
LONDON · CHAPMAN & HALL, LIMITED

Printed in the United States of America

PREFACE

This textbook is intended for a six semester-hour course in higher algebra for the undergraduate who has had two years of college mathematics including calculus. Although practically no knowledge of calculus is needed, the mathematical maturity developed by its study is necessary. It is my belief that it is both mathematically necessary and culturally desirable to introduce the undergraduate at an early stage to some of the simpler algebraic concepts that are as much a part of mathematics today as are the elementary concepts of calculus. Consequently, such topics as groups, rings, fields, and matrices are given an equal place with the theory of equations. Naturally, part of the traditional material in the theory of equations, such as the approximations to real roots, has been omitted. I have found that the subject matter selected presents no more difficulty to the average student than does the traditional course in the theory of equations. Only the elements of each concept and theory have been given. The book is intended to serve merely as an introduction to algebraic concepts so that the undergraduate may have some idea of the kind of concepts used in that part of mathematics usually called algebra.

The presentation is somewhat the same as in an elementary course in calculus. Examples and exercises are given throughout. The student is expected to work exercises for each class meeting. The number of ideas introduced at one time has been kept to a minimum. Consequently, in the discussion of matrices, for example, the concept of a vector space has not been introduced —an important omission. In general, the presentation is intended for the average undergraduate who finds the more advanced texts in higher algebra too difficult to read.

The book begins with a discussion of the number system which emphasizes those properties that are to be used for illustrative material in the elementary theory of groups and rings and which orients the student to the algebraic point of view. The real numbers are almost completely neglected. The elementary properties of groups, rings, and fields are then developed. In order that the student may have simple examples and use a noncommutative operation, permutation groups are introduced in the chapter on groups. The course proceeds with the elementary properties of polynomials over a field, emphasizing their analogy with the properties of integers. The elementary theory of matrices over a field including the application to the solution of simultaneous linear equations over a field is developed before determinants are introduced as values associated with square matrices. The theory of determinants and its connection with matrices then follow. The book closes with a chapter that introduces the student to factor groups, residue class rings, and the homomorphism theory of groups and rings.

In an address given before the Mathematical Association of America in 1939 ("Algebra for the Undergraduate," *American Mathematical Monthly*, Vol. 46, pp. 635–642, 1939), I first outlined the material for such a course, which I then had given for several years to juniors. My indebtedness at that time to the standard textbooks in higher algebra, particularly B. L. van der Waerden's *Moderne Algebra*, A. A. Albert's *Modern Higher Algebra*, and H. Hasse's *Höhere Algebra*, was evident. The more recent excellent expositions given in G. Birkhoff and S. MacLane's *A Survey of Modern Algebra* and in C. C. MacDuffee's two books, *An Introduction to Abstract Algebra* and *Vectors and Matrices*, have influenced my selection of proofs. Mention should also be made of the standard textbooks in number theory, group theory, and theory of equations. My students over a period of years have by their criticisms and difficulties helped me in making choices of methods of exposition. I am also indebted to Professor M. Gweneth Humphreys, who read the first draft of the manuscript and made many helpful suggestions.

MARIE J. WEISS

NEW ORLEANS, LOUISIANA
October 10, 1948

CONTENTS

1

The Integers

1 · The positive integers

The mathematical symbols first encountered by everyone are those of the positive integers: $1, 2, 3, \cdots$. These are often called the natural numbers. Their properties are familiar to all, and we shall list them systematically. It is not our purpose to develop these properties from a minimum number of hypotheses and undefined terms but rather to list those laws and properties that have long been familiar to the student and to use them as a characterizing definition of the positive integers.

The familiar operations on the positive integers are those of addition and multiplication; that is, for every pair of positive integers a, b we know what is meant by the sum $a + b$ and the product ab and that the sum and product are again positive integers. The fact that the sum and product of any two positive integers are again positive integers is often expressed by saying that the set of positive integers is *closed* under addition and multiplication. As is well known, the positive integers $a, b, c, \cdots$ obey the following laws governing these operations:

the commutative law

for addition $\qquad\qquad\qquad a + b = b + a,$

for multiplication $\qquad\qquad ab = ba;$

the associative law

for addition $\qquad\qquad a + (b + c) = (a + b) + c,$

for multiplication $\qquad\qquad a(bc) = (ab)c;$

the distributive law $\qquad\qquad a(b + c) = ab + ac.$

Note the meaning of the parentheses in the associative and

distributive laws, and note that, if the commutative law for multiplication did not hold, it would be necessary to have a second or right-hand distributive law, $(b + c)a = ba + ca$. As we see, however, this result could be obtained from the distributive law by applying the commutative law for multiplication to both sides of the equality. We shall study systems in which some of these laws do not hold, and therefore it is necessary to have a clear understanding of their meaning. Let us illustrate them with a few examples:

The equality

$$7(3 \cdot 6) = 6(3 \cdot 7)$$

holds, for, by first applying the associative law and then applying the commutative law for multiplication twice, we have

$$7(3 \cdot 6) = (7 \cdot 3)6 = 6(7 \cdot 3) = 6(3 \cdot 7).$$

Again, if a, b, c are positive integers, the equality

$$a(b + c) = ca + ab$$

holds, for, applying in succession the distributive law, the commutative law for addition, and the commutative law for multiplication, we have

$$a(b + c) = ab + ac = ac + ab = ca + ab.$$

An illustration of a system in which some of these laws do not hold can be given by arbitrarily defining an addition and a multiplication for positive integers as follows: Denote the new addition by $\oplus$ and the new multiplication by $\odot$. Let $a \oplus b = 2a$ and $a \odot b = 2ab$, where $2a$ and $2ab$ denote the results of ordinary multiplication. Then

$$b \oplus a = 2b, \quad b \odot a = 2ba, \quad a \oplus (b \oplus c) = a \oplus 2b = 2a,$$

$$(a \oplus b) \oplus c = 2a \oplus c = 4a, \quad a \odot (b \odot c) = a \odot 2bc = 4abc,$$

$$(a \odot b) \odot c = 2ab \odot c = 4abc, \quad a \odot (b \oplus c) = a \odot 2b = 4ab,$$

$$(a \odot b) \oplus (a \odot c) = 2ab \oplus 2ac = 4ab.$$

Note that the commutative and associative laws fail for addition but hold for multiplication. Are there two distributive laws in this system?

Exercises

1. Reduce the left-hand side of the following equalities to the right-hand side by using successively one associative, commutative, or distributive law:

a) $(3 + 5) + 6 = 3 + (5 + 6)$.

b) $1 + 5 = 5 + 1$.

c) $2(3 \cdot 5) = (2 \cdot 3)5$.

d) $2(3 \cdot 5) = 5(2 \cdot 3)$.

e) $6(8 + 4) = 4 \cdot 6 + 6 \cdot 8$.

f) $6(8 \cdot 4) = (4 \cdot 6)8$.

g) $3(7 + 5) = 5 \cdot 3 + 7 \cdot 3$.

h) $5(6 + 3) = 3 \cdot 5 + 5 \cdot 6$.

i) $6(5 \cdot 3) = (3 \cdot 6)5$.

j) $4 \cdot 6 + 7 \cdot 4 = 4(7 + 6)$.

k) $a[b + (c + d)] = (ab + ac) + ad$.

l) $a[b(cd)] = (bc)(ad)$.

m) $a[b(cd)] = (ab)(cd)$.

n) $(ad + ca) + ag = a[(g + c) + d]$.

2. Determine whether the operations $\oplus$ and $\odot$ for positive integers x, y defined as follows obey the commutative, associative, and distributive laws:

a) $x \oplus y = x + 2y$, $x \odot y = 2xy$.

b) $x \oplus y = x + y^2$, $x \odot y = xy^2$.

c) $x \oplus y = x^2 + y^2$, $x \odot y = x^2y^2$.

2 · Further properties

Some further properties of the positive integers will be listed. Note that the positive integer 1 is the only positive integer such that $1 \cdot a = a$, for every positive integer a. We say that 1 is an *identity* for multiplication. Again the following *cancellation* laws for addition and multiplication hold:

1) if $a + x = b + x$, then $a = b$;

2) if $ax = bx$, then $a = b$.

Moreover, for any two positive integers a and b, either $a = b$, or there exists a positive integer x such that $a + x = b$, or there exists a positive integer y such that $a = b + y$.

From these alternative relations between two positive integers, we can define *inequalities*. If $a + x = b$, we write $a < b$ (read a less than b) and $b > a$ (read b greater than a). Hence, for any two positive integers, we have the following mutually exclusive alternatives—either $a = b$, or $a < b$, or $a > b$—and we have established an order relation between any two positive integers. From the above definition we may prove the familiar properties of inequalities for positive integers:

   1) if $a < b$ and $b < c$, then $a < c$;
   2) if $a < b$, then $a + c < b + c$;
   3) if $a < b$, then $ac < bc$.

Their proof is left to the student.

3 · Finite induction

We come now to the last important property of the positive integers that will be discussed. This property will enable us to make proofs by the method known as *finite induction* or *mathematical induction*.

Postulate of finite induction. A set S of positive integers with the following *two* properties contains *all* the positive integers:

   a) the set S contains the positive integer 1;

   b) if the set S contains the positive integer k, it contains the positive integer $k + 1$.

This postulate is used to prove either true or false certain propositions that involve all positive integers. The proof is said to be made by finite induction.

First method of proof by finite induction. Let $P(n)$ be a proposition that is defined for every positive integer n. If $P(1)$ is true, and if $P(k + 1)$ is true whenever $P(k)$ is true, then $P(n)$ is true for all positive integers n.

The proof is immediate by the postulate of finite induction. For consider the set S of positive integers for which the proposition $P(n)$ is true. By hypothesis it contains the positive integer 1 and the positive integer $k + 1$ whenever it contains the positive integer k. Hence the set S contains all the positive integers.

Example. Let the power a^n, where n is a positive integer, be defined as follows: $a^1 = a$, $a^{k+1} = a^k \cdot a$. Prove that $(ab)^n = a^n b^n$.

If $n = 1$, we have $(ab)^1 = ab = a^1 b^1$ by the definition. Assume that this law of exponents holds for $n = k$: $(ab)^k = a^k b^k$. Then $(ab)^k(ab) = (ab)^{k+1}$ by definition, and $(ab)^k(ab) = (a^k b^k)(ab)$ by assumption. Applying the associative and commutative laws to the right-hand side of the last equation and using the definition, we have $(ab)^k(ab) = (a^k a)(b^k b) = a^{k+1} b^{k+1}$, which was to be proved. Hence this law of exponents is true for all positive integers n.

Closely allied to the postulate of finite induction is the principle of the smallest integer: In every nonempty set of positive integers there is a smallest integer. This principle can be proved from the postulate of finite induction.* We use this principle to establish the *Second method of proof by finite induction.* Let $P(n)$ be a proposition defined for every positive integer n. If $P(1)$ is true, and if, for each m, $P(m)$ is true whenever $P(k)$ is true for all positive integers $k < m$, then $P(n)$ is true for all positive integers n.

Let S be the set of positive integers for which $P(n)$ is false. If S is not empty it will contain a smallest positive integer m. Note that $m \neq 1$, for by hypothesis $P(1)$ is true. Hence, for all positive integers $k < m$, $P(k)$ is true. From our induction hypothesis we then have $P(m)$ true, but m is in the set S. Hence the set S is empty.

Exercises

Prove by finite induction for all positive integers n.

1. Use the definition given in the above example to prove the following laws:

$$\text{a) } 1^n = 1. \quad \text{b) } a^m a^n = a^{m+n}. \quad \text{c) } (a^m)^n = a^{mn}.$$

2. $4 + 8 + 12 + \cdots + 4n = 2n(n+1)$.
3. $3 \cdot 6 + 6 \cdot 9 + 9 \cdot 12 + \cdots + 3n(3n+3) = 3n(n+1)(n+2)$.
4. $6 \cdot 1^2 + 6 \cdot 2^2 + 6 \cdot 3^2 + \cdots + 6n^2 = n(n+1)(2n+1)$.
5. $3 \cdot 1 \cdot 2 + 3 \cdot 2 \cdot 3 + 3 \cdot 3 \cdot 4 + \cdots + 3n(n+1) = n(n+1)(n+2)$.

4 · Summary

For the sake of reference we shall now list the properties of the positive integers which fully characterize them. They may be used as a set of postulates for the positive integers.

The system of positive integers has the following properties:

1) The set of positive integers is closed under the two operations addition and multiplication. These operations obey the commutative, associative, and distributive laws.

2) The positive integer 1 has the property $1 \cdot a = a$ for every positive integer a.

* For a proof see Paul Dubreil, *Algèbre*, Vol. 1, p. 272, or E. Landau, *Grundlagen der Analysis*, p. 13.

3) The cancellation laws hold:

$$\text{if } a + x = b + x, \text{ then } a = b;$$
$$\text{if } ax = bx, \text{ then } a = b.$$

4) For any two positive integers a and b, either $a = b$, or there exists a positive integer x such that $a + x = b$, or there exists a positive integer y such that $a = b + y$.

5) The postulate of finite induction holds.

5 · The integers

We are familiar with the fact that given any two positive integers a and b we cannot always find a positive integer x such that $a + x = b$. This unsatisfactory state of affairs was remedied long ago by the introduction of the negative integers and zero to make up the system of integers. We introduce a new symbol, namely a pair of positive integers (a, b), and we shall use this new symbol to define an integer. Note the omission of the word positive. This new symbol has no meaning, of course, until we assign it properties.

Definition of equality. The equality $(a, b) = (c, d)$ holds if and only if $a + d = b + c$. Although this is not the ordinary concept of equality, the identity of symbols, we shall show that it has the usual properties of the equality sign.

Theorem 1. The equality (a, b) = (c, d) *is*

1) reflexive: (a, b) = (a, b);

2) symmetric: *if* (a, b) = (c, d), *then* (c, d) = (a, b);

3) transitive: *if* (a, b) = (c, d) *and if* (c, d) = (e, f), *then* (a, b) = (e, f).

These properties are readily proved from the definition of equality and the properties of the positive integers. Since $a + b = b + a$, 1) holds. If $a + d = b + c$, then $c + b = d + a$ and 2) holds. In 3) we wish to prove that $a + f = b + e$, given that $a + d = b + c$ and $c + f = d + e$. Now $(a + d) + f = (b + c) + f = b + (c + f) = b + (d + e)$. Thus $(a + f) + d = (b + e) + d$, and hence by the cancellation law for the addition of positive integers $a + f = b + e$.

Any relation between pairs of elements, such as the above equality of pairs of positive integers, that is reflexive, symmetric, and transitive is called an *equivalence relation*. Note that this equivalence relation or equality separates the set of pairs of positive integers into mutually exclusive classes of pairs such that any two members of a class are equivalent or equal, whereas members from different classes are nonequivalent or unequal. An integer is defined to be a class of equivalent pairs.

Definition of addition and multiplication. We define the sum

$$(a, b) + (c, d) = (a + c, b + d)$$

and the product

$$(a, b) \cdot (c, d) = (ac + bd, ad + bc).$$

These definitions of the sum and the product of two pairs (a, b) and (c, d) are really definitions of the sum and product of the class of pairs containing (a, b) and the class of pairs containing (c, d). For we can substitute any pair $(a', b') = (a, b)$ and any pair $(c', d') = (c, d)$ in the above definitions and obtain a sum pair

$$(a' + c', b' + d') = (a + c, b + d)$$

and a product pair

$$(a' c' + b' d', a' d' + b' c') = (ac + bd, ad + bc).$$

For example, if $(a', b') = (a, b)$ and $(c', d') = (c, d)$, we have $a' + b = b' + a$, $c' + d = d' + c$, and hence

$$(a' + c') + (b + d) = (b' + d') + (a + c).$$

Consequently,

$$(a', b') + (c', d') = (a' + c', b' + d') = (a + c, b + d).$$

By a slightly more involved manipulation, we can also prove that $(a', b') \cdot (c', d') = (a, b) \cdot (c, d)$. Thus the definitions of sum and product of two pairs (a, b) and (c, d) determine two classes of pairs, the sum and product classes, which are determined by the classes containing (a, b) and (c, d). We have thus defined the sum and product of two integers.

It is easily proved that addition and multiplication obey the commutative, associative, and distributive laws. For example, the distributive law can be proved as follows:

$$(a, b) \cdot [(c, d) + (e, f)] = (a, b) \cdot (c + e, d + f)$$
$$= (a[c + e] + b[d + f], a[d + f] + b[c + e])$$
$$= ([ac + bd] + [ae + bf], [ad + bc] + [af + be])$$
$$= (ac + bd, ad + bc) + (ae + bf, af + be)$$
$$= (a, b) \cdot (c, d) + (a, b) \cdot (e, f).$$

Note that in the above proof we used not only the definitions of the new addition and multiplication but also the associative, commutative, and distributive properties of the positive integers. The proofs of the other laws are left to the student.

6 · The number zero

Now let us investigate more closely the pairs (a, b) with respect to the order relation between the positive integers a and b.   Recall that either $a = b$, or $a > b$, or $a < b$.   Thus any pair (a, b) may be written either as (a, a), or $(x + b, b)$, or $(a, x + a)$.

We consider first the properties of the pairs (a, a).   We note that $(a, a) = (b, b)$.   Moreover, if $(a, a) = (b, c)$, then $b = c$, for by the definition of equality $a + c = a + b$.   Thus the pairs in which both positive integers are equal determine a class that may be represented by the pair (a, a) but that is independent of the particular integer a.   We shall call this class the integer zero, and we shall represent it by any pair in which both positive integers are equal.

Properties of zero.   For every pair (x, y)

$$(x, y) + (a, a) = (x, y)$$

and

$$(x, y) \cdot (a, a) = (a, a).$$

These two properties follow immediately from the definitions, for

$$(x, y) + (a, a) = (x + a, y + a) = (x, y)$$

and

$$(x, y) \cdot (a, a) = (ax + ay, ax + ay) = (a, a).$$

The first property listed is often characterized by saying that zero is an *identity for addition*.

7 · The positive integers as a subset of the integers

We now need to define a *one-to-one correspondence* between two sets of symbols. We say that there is a one-to-one correspondence between the elements of a set A and the elements of a set B if the elements of the two sets can be paired so that to each element of A there corresponds one and only one element of the set B and if each element of B is the correspondent or image of one and only one element of A. For example, there is a one-to-one correspondence between the set of chairs in a classroom and the set of students in the classroom if there is a chair for each student and if there is a student for each chair.

Now consider the pairs $(x + b, b)$. We note that $(x + b, b) = (x + c, c)$. Moreover, $(x + b, b) = (y + c, c)$ only if $x = y$. Hence only one distinct integer is represented by all the pairs $(x + b, b)$, where x is fixed and b is any positive integer. Thus we may set up a one-to-one correspondence between the classes represented by the pairs $(x + b, b)$ and the positive integers as follows. We shall denote the correspondence by writing

$$(x + b, b) \leftrightarrow x.$$

Thus to each class represented by $(x + b, b)$, where x is fixed, we assign the positive integer x, and to each positive integer x we assign the class represented by $(x + b, b)$. Now if

$$(x + b, b) \leftrightarrow x \quad \text{and} \quad (y + c, c) \leftrightarrow y$$

then

$$(x + b, b) + (y + c, c) = (x + y + b + c, b + c) \leftrightarrow x + y^*$$

and

$$(x + b, b) \cdot (y + c, c) =$$
$$(xy + xc + by + bc + bc, xc + by + bc + bc) \leftrightarrow xy.$$

Such a one-to-one correspondence in which addition and multiplication are preserved is called an *isomorphism*. Thus we see that the classes of pairs (a, b) for which $a > b$ may be regarded as merely different symbols for the positive integers, for they have exactly the same properties as the positive integers. To summarize, we have proved the following theorem.

---

* To save space we shall no longer indicate the use of the associative law for addition for positive integers by means of parentheses. The meaning of $a + b + c$ is now clear.

Theorem 2.   The classes of pairs (a, b), *with* a > b, *are isomorphic to the positive integers.*

8 · The negative integers

So far then we have introduced by means of our new symbols (a, b) only one essentially new number, namely zero.   The third type of pairs (a, b), with $a < b$, then, represent numbers other than zero and the positive integers.   They may be written in the form $(a, x + a)$, and as in the case of the pairs $(x + b, b)$ only one distinct class or integer is represented by the pairs $(a, x + a)$, where x is fixed and a is any positive integer.   We shall call these classes of pairs *negative integers.*

Thus we have extended our number system.   Since a subset of the classes of pairs of positive integers may be identified with the positive integers, we say that the positive integers have been embedded in the system of integers.   Moreover, we may now find a solution x in the system of integers for the equation $a + x = b$, where a and b denote integers.   We first prove the following cancellation laws.

Theorem 3.   If (a, b) + (c, d) = (a, b) + (e, f), *then* (c, d) = (e, f).   *If* (x, y) · (a, b) = (x, y) · (c, d) *and* (x, y) ≠ (z, z), *then* (a, b) = (c, d).

The cancellation law for addition is easily proved by using the cancellation law for positive integers.   We are given $(a + c, b + d) = (a + e, b + f)$.   Hence $a + c + b + f = b + d + a + e$ and $c + f = d + e$, which gives $(c, d) = (e, f)$.

To prove the cancellation law for multiplication, suppose first that (x, y) represents a negative integer and let $y = x + z$.   Then $(x, x + z) · (a, b) = (x, x + z) · (c, d)$.   Performing the multiplication, and using the definition of equality and finally the cancellation laws for positive integers, we have the desired result $b + c = a + d$.   The proof when (x, y) represents a positive integer is similar.

Theorem 4.   The equation (a, b) + (x, y) = (c, d) *has a unique solution.*

Note that $(a, b) + (c + b, d + a) = (a + c + b, b + d + a) = (c, d)$.   Hence $(c + b, d + a)$ is a solution.   Now let (u, v) be any

solution.   Then $(a, b) + (c + b, d + a) = (a, b) + (u, v)$, and, by
the cancellation law for addition, we have $(u, v) = (c + b, d + a)$.

The solution $(x, y) = (c + b, d + a)$ is known as the difference
$(c, d) - (a, b)$, and the operation of forming this difference is
called subtraction.   In particular, the solution (x, y) of the equation $(a, b) + (x, y) = (z, z)$ is $(z, z) - (a, b) = (z + b, z + a) =$
(b, a).   It will be denoted by $-(a, b)$, and $-(a, b)$ is known as
the *additive inverse* of (a, b).

Since any relations between integers can be proved by using representatives of the classes of pairs defining the integers, Theorems
3 and 4 give us the cancellation laws for integers and the unique
solution of the equation $a + x = b$, where a, x, and b denote
integers.   Moreover, the definition of the minus sign just given
can be applied to the class or integer represented by the pair (a, b).
The familiar properties of the minus sign can thus be proved for
integers by using representatives from the classes defining the
integers.   For simplicity let us henceforth denote an integer by
the single symbol y and its additive inverse by $-y$.   Zero will be
denoted by the usual symbol 0.

Exercises

1. Complete the proof of Theorem 3.
2. $-(-y) = y$. [Let (a, b) represent y. Then $-(a, b) = (b, a)$ represents
$-y$, and $-(b, a) = (a, b)$ represents $-(-y)$. Hence $-(-y) = y$.]
3. $(-x)(-y) = xy$.   4. $(-x)y = x(-y) = -xy$.
5. $-(x + y) = (-x) + (-y)$.   6. $x(y - z) = xy - xz$.
7. $(x - y) + (y - z) = x - z$.
8. Prove that the negative integers are not isomorphic to the positive
integers.
9. Prove: If $xy = 0$, then $x = 0$ or $y = 0$.
10. Prove by induction for positive integers n:

a) $1 + 3 + \cdots + (2n - 1) = n^2$.
b) $1 + 5 + \cdots + (4n - 3) = n(2n - 1)$.
c) $1^3 + 3^3 + \cdots + (2n - 1)^3 = n^2(2n^2 - 1)$.
d) $2 + 2^2 + 2^3 + \cdots + 2^n = 2(2^n - 1)$.
e) $1 \cdot 2 + 2 \cdot 2^2 + 3 \cdot 2^3 + \cdots + n \cdot 2^n = (n - 1)2^{n+1} + 2$.

9 · Inequalities

We now define inequalities between integers in terms of the
positive integers.   The integer a is said to be less than the integer
b or the integer b is said to be greater than the integer a if and only

if $b - a$ is a positive integer. We write $a < b$ or $b > a$. The following properties of the inequality sign for integers can be proved from the definition:

1) if $a < b$ and $b < c$, then $a < c$;
2) if $a < b$, then $a + c < b + c$;
3) if $a < b$ and $c > 0$, then $ac < bc$;
4) if $a < b$ and $c < 0$, then $ac > bc$.

Absolute value. For a given integer a, either $a = 0$, or $a > 0$, or $-a > 0$. Thus we define the absolute value of a : $|a| = 0$, or a, or $-a$, according as $a = 0$, $a > 0$, or $-a > 0$. The two properties of the absolute value sign that we shall need are

$$|a| \cdot |b| = |ab| \quad \text{and} \quad |a + b| \leq |a| + |b|,$$

and they may easily be proved by a consideration of the various possibilities for a and b as positive or negative integers or zero. As an example, we shall prove the second inequality. If a and b are both positive or both negative, or if at least one is zero, we easily see that the equality sign holds. If a is positive and b is negative, we have $|a| = a$ and $|b| = -b$. Then, if $a + b$ is negative, $|a + b| = -(a + b)$, but $-(a + b) < a - b = |a| + |b|$. If $a + b$ is nonnegative, $|a + b| = a + b$, and $a + b < a - b$. We merely interchange the roles of a and b if a is negative and b is positive.

Exercises

1. Prove that $|a| \cdot |b| = |ab|$.
2. If $xy = 1$, then $x = \pm 1$ and $y = \pm 1$.

10 · Division of integers

We have seen that the set of integers is closed with respect to addition, subtraction, and multiplication. However, the set of integers is not closed with respect to division. Division is defined as follows:

Definition of division. An integer a is said to be divisible by an integer b if there exists an integer c such that $a = bc$. We write $b \mid a$, and say that b is a divisor of a and a is a multiple of b.

From the property $a \cdot 0 = 0$ for all integers a, we conclude that every integer divides zero and that zero divides zero.

The student, however, should note that zero plays a unique role in the concept of division, for, if b is not zero in the definition given, the integer c is unique. We also note that division is reflexive and transitive. For $a \mid a$, and, moreover, if $a \mid b$ and $b \mid c$, then integers x and y exist such that $ax = b$ and $by = c$, so that $a(xy) = c$ and $a \mid c$.

Associates. Two nonzero integers a and b are called associates if both $a \mid b$ and $b \mid a$. Since $a = bc$ and $b = ad$, $a = adc$. By the cancellation law for multiplication $dc = 1$, and hence $d = \pm 1$ and $c = \pm 1$. Thus the only associates of a are $\pm a$.

Units. An associate of the integer 1 is called a unit. Hence the only units are ± 1.

Primes. A nonzero integer p is a prime if it is neither ± 1 and if its only divisors are ± 1 and $\pm p$.

Exercises

1. Find the divisors of 24.
2. List the first 15 positive primes.
3. Find the positive prime divisors of 112.
4. Prove: If $a \mid b$ and $a \mid c$, then $a \mid (b + c)$.
5. If $b \mid a$ and $a \neq 0$, then $|b| \leq |a|$.
6. If $b \mid a$ and $|a| < |b|$, then $a = 0$.

11 · Greatest common divisor

Theorem 5. The division algorithm. Given two integers a *and* b, *with* b $\neq 0$, *then there exists a unique pair of integers* q *and* r *such that* a = bq + r, *where* $0 \leq$ r $< |b|$.

Consider the set of integers $a - bx$. It contains at least one nonnegative integer, namely, $a - |a|b$ if $b < 0$ and $a - (-|a|)b$ if $b > 0$. For if $b < 0$, $b \leq -1$ and $|a|b \leq -|a| \leq a$, whereas, if $b > 0$, $b \geq 1$ and $-|a|b \leq -|a| \leq a$. Thus the set contains either zero or a smallest positive integer. Let this smallest nonnegative integer be $r = a - bq$. Now $r \geq 0$, and, if $r \geq |b|$, then $0 \leq r - |b| = a - bq - |b| = a - (q \pm 1)b < r$, contrary to the choice of r. Thus the existence of the desired integers r and q has been established. The integer r is called the *remainder*, and the integer q the *quotient*. To prove the uniqueness of q and r we assume that there is a second set of integers q' and r' such that $a = bq' + r'$, where $0 \leq r' < |b|$. Then $bq' + r' = bq + r$, and $r' - r = (q - q')b$, which says that b divides $r' - r$, but

$|r' - r| < |b|$. Hence $r' - r = 0$, and, since $b \neq 0$, $q' - q = 0$.

Greatest common divisor. An integer d is called a greatest common divisor of two integers a and b if $d \mid a$ and $d \mid b$, and, if c is any common divisor of a and b, $c \mid d$. It is easy to see that, if either a or b is zero, then the nonzero integer is a greatest common divisor. If both a and b are zero, then zero is the greatest common divisor, since every integer divides zero. Further note that according to the definition any two greatest common divisors of two nonzero integers must be associates. Hence, if two nonzero integers a and b have a greatest common divisor, they have a positive greatest common divisor, which we shall denote by (a, b) and call the g.c.d.

Theorem 6. The euclidean algorithm. Any two nonzero integers a and b have a positive greatest common divisor.

The proof will also give us a method for finding the greatest common divisor. Since any two greatest common divisors of a and b are associates, it may be assumed that both a and b are positive. Write $a = bq + r$, $0 \leq r < b$. If $r = 0$, then b is the g.c.d. of a and b. If $r \neq 0$, we prove that $(a, b) = (b, r)$. Let $d = (a, b)$ and $d' = (b, r)$. Now d divides a, b, and $a - bq$. Hence d divides r and is a common divisor of b and r. Thus $d \mid d'$. Similarly, d' divides b, r, and $bq + r$. Thus d' divides a and is a common divisor of a and b. Hence $d' \mid d$. Therefore $d = d'$, and we have reduced the problem of finding the greatest common divisor of a and b to that of finding the greatest common divisor of b and r.

Now apply the division algorithm to b and r, obtaining $b = rq_1 + r_1$, $0 \leq r_1 < r$. If $r_1 = 0$, r is the g.c.d. of b and r. If $r_1 \neq 0$, $(b, r) = (r, r_1)$, and the problem of finding the g.c.d. of b and r has been reduced to that of finding the g.c.d. of r and r_1. Continuing in this manner, we obtain the following equations:

$$a = bq + r, \quad 0 < r < b,$$
$$b = rq_1 + r_1, \quad 0 < r_1 < r,$$
$$r = r_1q_2 + r_2, \quad 0 < r_2 < r_1,$$
$$\dots\dots\dots\dots\dots\dots\dots\dots$$
$$r_j = r_{j+1}q_{j+2} + r_{j+2}, \quad 0 < r_{j+2} < r_{j+1}.$$

Since the r_j form a decreasing set of nonnegative integers, there must exist an r_{n+1} equal to zero. Hence

$$r_{n-2} = r_{n-1}q_n + r_n, \quad 0 < r_n < r_{n-1},$$
$$r_{n-1} = r_n q_{n+1}.$$

Now $(a, b) = (b, r) = (r, r_1) = \cdots = (r_{n-1}, r_n) = r_n$. Thus the greatest common divisor of a and b is r_n.

Theorem 7. *If* $d = (a, b)$, *there exist integers* m *and* n *such that* $d = ma + nb$.

This theorem can be proved by expressing the successive remainders r_j, obtained by the euclidean algorithm, in terms of a and b as indicated below:

$$r = a - bq = a + (-q)b,$$
$$r_1 = b - rq_1 = b - (a - bq)q_1 = (-q_1)a + (1 + qq_1)b, \text{ etc.}$$

A general proof can be made by induction. Denote r by r_0 and q by q_0. Now assume that $r_j = m_j a + n_j b$, where m_j and n_j are integers, for all nonnegative integers $j < k$. We have checked that this equation holds for $j = 0$ and $j = 1$. Then, from the euclidean algorithm and our induction hypothesis, we have

$$r_k = r_{k-2} - r_{k-1}q_k$$
$$= m_{k-2}a + n_{k-2}b - (m_{k-1}a + n_{k-1}b)q_k$$
$$= (m_{k-2} - m_{k-1}q_k)a + (n_{k-2} - n_{k-1}q_k)b,$$

and our proof is completed. Thus r_n can be expressed as a linear function of a and b with integral coefficients.

Example. Find the g.c.d. of 595 and 252, and express it in the form $252m + 595n$. We have $595 = 2(252) + 91, 252 = 2(91) + 70, 91 = 70 + 21, 70 = 3(21) + 7, 21 = 3(7)$. Thus $(252, 595) = 7$. To find m and n, we proceed as follows: $91 = 595 - 2(252)$, $70 = 252 - 2[595 - 2(252)] = 5(252) - 2(595), 21 = 3(595) - 7(252), 7 = 70 - 3(21) = 26(252) - 11(595)$. Hence $m = 26$ and $n = -11$. The student should note that m and n are not unique. For example, $7 = (26 + 595)252 - (11 + 252)595 = 621(252) - 263(595)$.

Exercises

1. Find $(294, 273)$, and express it in the form $294m + 273n$ in two ways.
2. Find $(163, 34)$, and express it in the form $163m + 34n$ in two ways.

$$d = ma + nb$$
$$d = (m+b)a + (m-a)b$$

3. Find (6432, 132), and express it in the form $132m + 6432n$.

4. Find (3456, 7234).

5. Prove that, if $m > 0$, $(ma, mb) = m(a, b)$.

12 · Prime factors

Theorem 8.   If p *is a prime and if* p $|$ ab, a *and* b *integers, then* p $|$ a *or* p $|$ b.

Since p is a prime its only divisors are ± 1 and $\pm p$. Therefore, if p does not divide a, the g.c.d. of a and p is 1. By the previous theorem there exist integers m and n such that $1 = ma + np$. Now $b = mab + npb$. Since p is a factor of the right-hand side of this equation, it divides b by definition, and the theorem is proved.

Corollary.   If p *is a prime and divides the product of integers* $a_1 a_2 \cdots a_n$, *then* p *divides one of the integers* a_i.

Repeated application of the preceding theorem gives this result immediately.

Definition.   If $(a, b) = 1$, the two integers a and b are said to be relatively prime.

Theorem 9.   If (a, b) $= 1$ *and if* b $|$ ac, *then* b $|$ c.

The proof is similar to the proof of the preceding theorem, for by hypothesis there exist integers m and n such that $1 = ma + nb$, and hence $c = mac + nbc$.

Theorem 10.   Unique factorization theorem for integers.   Every integer a, $|a| > 1$, *can be expressed as a unit times a product of positive primes.   This representation is unique except for the order in which the prime factors occur.*

Let a be the integer to be factored. If a is a prime, the integer has been represented according to the theorem. Therefore, let a be composite, i.e., neither a unit nor a prime. Now assume the theorem true for all integers less than $|a|$. Since a is composite, $|a| = |b| \cdot |c|$, where $|b|$ and $|c|$ are integers less than $|a|$. Hence by the induction hypothesis $|b| = p_1 p_2 \cdots p_s$ and $|c| = q_1 q_2 \cdots q_t$, where p_i and q_j are positive primes. Thus

$$|a| = |b| \cdot |c| = p_1 p_2 \cdots p_s q_1 q_2 \cdots q_t,$$

and it remains to be proved that the representation is unique except for the order in which the prime factors occur. Suppose there were a second factorization $|a| = p_1'p_2' \cdots p_v'$. Then $p_1'p_2' \cdots p_v' = p_1p_2 \cdots p_sq_1q_2 \cdots q_t$. Now by the previous corollary p_1' divides one of these primes p_1, say. Thus

$$p_2'p_3' \cdots p_v' = p_2 \cdots p_sq_1 \cdots q_t.$$

Reapplying the same reasoning to these equal products a finite number of times, we obtain $v = s + t$ and thus a unique factorization of $|a|$ and hence of a.

Note that the theorem does not exclude the occurrence of equal primes. Hence we may write the integer

$$a = \pm p_1^{a_1}p_2^{a_2} \cdots p_n^{a_n}, \text{ where } 1 < p_1 < p_2 < \cdots < p_n,$$

and we have proved that the exponents a_i as well as the primes are uniquely determined.

Exercises

1. Illustrate the unique factorization theorem for the integers 576, −321, and 5244.

2. What can you conclude about the g.c.d. of a and b if integers x and y exist such that $ax + by = 1$? if $ax + by = 3$?

3. If $d = (a, b)$, $a = a_1d$, $b = b_1d$, then $(a_1, b_1) = 1$.

4. If $(a, b) = 1$, and $a \mid c$ and $b \mid c$, then $ab \mid c$.

5. Prove that $2m^2 = n^2$ is an impossible equation in integers when $(m, n) = 1$.

6. If $(a, b) = 1$, then $(a + b, a - b) = 2$ or 1.

7. If $(c, d) = 1$, then $(c^n, d) = 1$, where n is a positive integer.

8. Prove that the number of primes is infinite. Hint: Assume that the number of primes is finite and form their product $p_1p_2 \cdots p_n$. Then consider the integer $p_1p_2 \cdots p_n + 1$.

9. Show that $2^{2n} + 1$ is divisible by 5 for n a positive odd integer.

10. Show that $2^{2n} - 1$ is divisible by 5 for n a positive even integer.

13 · Congruences

Definition. Two integers a and b are said to be congruent modulo an integer m if and only if there exists an integer k such that $a - b = km$. Note that this definition merely says that m divides $a - b$. We write $a \equiv b \pmod{m}$, and m is called the modulus of the congruence. For example, $7 \equiv 15 \pmod 4$, for $7 - 15 = 4(-2)$.

Theorem 11. The relation, congruent modulo m, *is*

1) *reflexive*: a ≡ a (*mod* m),
2) *symmetric*: *if* a ≡ b (*mod* m), *then* b ≡ a (*mod* m),
3) *transitive*: *if* a ≡ b (*mod* m) *and* b ≡ c (*mod* m), *then* a ≡ c (*mod* m).

These properties follow immediately from the definition of a congruence. For example, we can prove transitivity as follows: Since $a - b = km$ and $b - c = nm$, we obtain $a - c = (k + n)m$ by addition, which is the result desired.

From this theorem we may expect that congruences behave in many respects like equalities. The following three theorems illustrate this similarity.

Theorem 12. If a ≡ b (*mod* m), *then* a + x ≡ b + x, *and* ax ≡ bx (*mod* m) *for all integers* x.

The proofs are again immediate from the definition and are left to the student.

Theorem 13. If a ≡ b *and* c ≡ d (*mod* m), *then* a + c ≡ b + d, a − c ≡ b − d, *and* ac ≡ bd (*mod* m).

Each of these statements can be proved directly from the definition. However, the last is proved more simply by using the second part of Theorem 12 and the transitive property of congruences as follows: $ac \equiv bc$ and $bc \equiv bd$ (mod m), and therefore $ac \equiv bd$ (mod m).

Theorem 14. If ca ≡ cb (*mod* m) *and* d = (c, m), *so that* m = dw, *then* a ≡ b (*mod* w).

Now $c = dv$ and $m = dw$, where $(v, w) = 1$. Moreover, $dw \mid c(a - b)$ and hence $w \mid v(a - b)$. Thus, since $(v, w) = 1$, $w \mid (a - b)$.

If $d = 1$ we obtain the following theorem.

Theorem 15. Let ca ≡ cb (*mod* m) *and* (c, m) = 1, *then* a ≡ b (*mod* m).

A useful alternative definition of congruence is incorporated in the following theorem.

Theorem 16. a ≡ b *(mod* m) *if and only if* a *and* b *leave the same remainder when divided by* m.

If $a \equiv b \pmod{m}$, then $b - a = km$. Let $a = mq + r$, $0 \leq r < |m|$. Now $b = a + km = mq + r + km = (q + k)m + r$, which states that r is the remainder when b is divided by m. On the other hand, if $a = mq + r$ and $b = mq_1 + r$, $0 \leq r < |m|$, then $a - b = (q - q_1)\, m$ and $a \equiv b \pmod{m}$.

Thus any integer a is congruent modulo m to its remainder r. Hence, by the transitive property of congruences, we may substitute r for a in any congruence modulo m. For example, if $313x \equiv 7 \pmod{10}$, then $3x \equiv 7 \pmod{10}$ is an equivalent statement, for $313 \equiv 3 \pmod{10}$, and $313x \equiv 3x \pmod{10}$.

Exercises

1. What does $a \equiv b \pmod{0}$ mean?

2. Find the least positive integers modulo 7 to which the integers 22, 312, and $22 \cdot 312$ are congruent.

3. Find the least positive integer modulo 11 to which the product $3 \cdot 7 \cdot 13 \cdot 515 \cdot 23$ is congruent.

4. Find the least positive integers modulo 5 to which the powers 3^2, 3^3, 3^4, 3^{10} are congruent.

5. Find the least positive integer modulo 7 to which 10^{515} is congruent.

6. If $14x \equiv 2 \pmod{8}$, quote theorems that enable us to write $7x \equiv 1 \pmod{4}$, $6x \equiv 2 \pmod{8}$, and $3x \equiv 1 \pmod{4}$.

7. If m is an integer, then $m^2 \equiv 0$ or $1 \pmod{4}$.

8. Recall that any integer may be expressed as follows:

$$\pm(a_n 10^n + a_{n-1}10^{n-1} + \cdots + a_1 10 + a_0),$$

where the a_i are integers 0 through 9. Hence show that, if an integer is divisible by 9, the sum of its digits is divisible by 9.

14 · The linear congruence

We shall now discuss the linear congruence $ax \equiv b \pmod{m}$. Note that, if x_1 is a solution, i.e., $ax_1 \equiv b \pmod{m}$, then any other integer $x_2 \equiv x_1 \pmod{m}$ is also a solution, for we have $ax_2 \equiv ax_1 \equiv b \pmod{m}$. We usually take integers in the interval $0 \leq x < |m|$ as representatives of the solutions.

Theorem 17. The congruence ax ≡ b *(mod* m) *has a solution if and only if the greatest common divisor* d *of* a *and* m *divides* b. *If* d *divides* b, *the congruence has exactly* d *incongruent solutions modulo* m.

Let $ax \equiv b \pmod{m}$ have a solution x_1. Then $ax_1 - b = km$, and $d = (a, m)$ necessarily divides b. Now given that d divides b, we seek solutions of the congruence. Since $d = (a, m)$, there exist integers x_1 and y_1 such that $ax_1 + my_1 = d$. Now $b = b_1d$, and multiplying the linear expression for d by b_1 we have $a(x_1b_1) + m(y_1b_1) = db_1 = b$. Thus x_1b_1 is a solution of the congruence $ax \equiv b \pmod{m}$.

It remains to be proved that there are d incongruent solutions modulo m. Now $m = m_1d$, and $a = a_1d$. Hence a solution x of the congruence $ax \equiv b \pmod{m}$ is also a solution of the congruence $a_1x \equiv b_1 \pmod{m_1}$, and conversely. Any two solutions of $a_1x \equiv b_1 \pmod{m_1}$ are congruent modulo m_1. For, let x_0 and x_1 be any two solutions. Then $a_1x_0 \equiv b_1 \equiv a_1x_1 \pmod{m_1}$, and, since $(a_1, m_1) = 1$, $x_0 \equiv x_1 \pmod{m_1}$. Hence all the incongruent solutions modulo m of $ax \equiv b \pmod{m}$ are found among the integers $x_0 + km_1$. We wish to show that the set of integers $x_0 + km_1$ contains d and only d incongruent integers modulo m, whose representatives are $x_0, x_0 + m_1, x_0 + 2m_1, \cdots, x_0 + (d - 1)m_1$. First, these representatives are all incongruent modulo m, for, if $x_0 + r_1m_1 \equiv x_0 + r_2m_1 \pmod{m}$, where $r_1 < d$ and $r_2 < d$, then $r_1m_1 \equiv r_2m_1 \pmod{m}$ and $r_1 \equiv r_2 \pmod{d}$; but $|r_1 - r_2| < d$, and hence $r_1 = r_2$. Next, any integer $x_0 + km_1$ is congruent to one of the above representatives, for $k = qd + r$, where $0 \leq r < d$, and $x_0 + km_1 = x_0 + (qd + r)m_1 \equiv x_0 + rm_1 \pmod{m}$.

In solving any linear congruence, first note how it may be simplified by using all the properties of congruences that have been developed. For example, $x + 50 \equiv 39 \pmod{7}$ is equivalent to $x + 1 \equiv 4 \pmod{7}$, and hence $x \equiv 3 \pmod{7}$. Again, if $235x \equiv 54 \pmod{7}$, then $4x \equiv 5 \pmod{7}$, and hence $x \equiv 3 \pmod{7}$. Again, if $29x \equiv 5 \pmod{34}$, then $-5x \equiv 5 \pmod{34}$ and $x \equiv -1 \pmod{34}$.

The congruence $35x \equiv 5 \pmod{14}$ is an example of a linear congruence without a solution, for $(35, 14) = 7$, and 7 does not divide 5. On the other hand, $35x \equiv 14 \pmod{21}$ has exactly 7 incongruent solutions modulo 21. In this case we divide through by 7, obtaining the congruence $5x \equiv 2 \pmod{3}$, which has 1 as its least positive solution. Hence representatives of the 7 incongruent solutions of $35x \equiv 14 \pmod{21}$ in the interval $0 \leq x < 21$ are 1, 4, 7, 10, 13, 16, and 19.

If the modulus is a large number, the greatest common divisor process enables us to find a solution as was shown in the proof of the general theorem. For example, in the congruence $11x \equiv 2$ (mod 317), $(317, 11) = 1$, and we find by solving for the remainders in the greatest common divisor process that $1 = 5(317) + 11(-144)$. Then $2 = 10(317) + 11(-288)$, and -288 is a solution. We take the least positive solution 29 as a representative solution.

Exercises

Find the incongruent solutions of the following congruences.

1. $x - 3 \equiv 2$ (mod 5).
2. $2x + 1 \equiv 4$ (mod 5).
3. $2x + 1 \equiv 4$ (mod 10).
4. $3x \equiv 2$ (mod 7).
5. $51x \equiv 32$ (mod 7).
6. $13x \equiv 10$ (mod 28).
7. $273x \equiv 210$ (mod 588).
8. $66x \equiv 8$ (mod 78).
9. $104x \equiv 16$ (mod 296).
10. $1183x \equiv 481$ (mod 533).
11. $572x \equiv 412$ (mod 516).
12. $45x \equiv 24$ (mod 348).

13. Prove that, if p is a prime and $c \not\equiv 0$ (mod p), then $cx \equiv b$ (mod p) has a unique solution modulo p.

14. Find integers x and y such that $313x + 45y = 17$.

15. If $(m_1, m_2) = 1$, then the congruences $x \equiv b$ (mod m_1) and $x \equiv c$ (mod m_2) have a common solution x. Any two solutions are congruent modulo $m_1 m_2$.

15 · Residue classes

Recall that any relation between pairs of elements that is reflexive, symmetric, and transitive is called an equivalence relation. Hence congruent modulo m is an equivalence relation between pairs of integers. Any equivalence relation between the elements of a set separates the elements into mutually exclusive classes of elements such that any two elements of a class are equivalent and elements from different classes are not equivalent. Thus we separate the integers into classes modulo m, putting into the same class all those integers that are congruent modulo m. We obtain m classes, for any integer is congruent modulo m to its remainder, and there are m remainders $0, 1, 2, \cdots, |m| - 1$. These classes, called residue classes modulo m, are the m sets of integers km, $km + 1, km + 2, \cdots, km + |m| - 1$, where k runs through all the integers. Denote these classes by $C_0, C_1, C_2, \cdots, C_{|m|-1}$, respectively.

Addition and multiplication of these residue classes can be defined as follows: The sum $C_i + C_j$ is the class that contains the sum of an integer from C_i and an integer from C_j. The product C_iC_j is the class that contains the product of an integer from the class C_i by an integer from the class C_j. Note that these sums and products are unique, for, if a_i and a_i' are any two integers from C_i, and if a_j and a_j' are any two integers from C_j, then, since $a_i \equiv a_i'$ and since $a_j \equiv a_j'$, $a_i + a_j \equiv a_i' + a_j'$ and $a_ia_j \equiv a_i'a_j'$ (mod m). From these definitions we can easily prove that addition and multiplication of residue classes obey the commutative, associative, and distributive laws. The proofs are left to the student.

Exercises

1. For the modulus 6:
   a) Calculate C_2C_3, $(C_4C_5)C_1$, $C_4(C_2 + C_3)$, $C_4C_3 + C_4C_2$.
   b) Find solutions C_x of the equations $C_2 + C_x = C_0$, $C_5C_x = C_1$, $C_i + C_x = C_j$.
   c) Has the equation $C_3C_x = C_2$ a solution?
   d) If $C_3C_x = C_3C_y$, can we conclude that $C_x = C_y$?
2. Answer the same questions for the modulus 7.
3. For the arbitrary modulus m find a solution C_x of the equation $C_i + C_x = C_j$.
4. For the arbitrary modulus m, has the equation $C_iC_x = C_j$ always a solution C_x?
5. Prove: $C_iC_j = C_0$ implies $C_i = C_0$ or $C_j = C_0$ if and only if the modulus m is a prime.

16 · Positional notation for integers

A direct application of the congruence properties of integers is the method used to represent any integer. Recall that any integer is represented by means of a signed sequence of the ten symbols 0, 1, 2, 3, $\cdots$, 9, namely the remainders modulo 10. This representation is obtained in the following way. Let a be a positive integer. By means of the division algorithm the integer a may be written in the form $a = 10q_0 + r_0$, $0 \le r_0 < 10$. If $q_0 = 0$, r_0 is the symbol used for a. If $q_0 > 0$, reapply the division algorithm to q_0, obtaining $q_0 = 10q_1 + r_1$, $0 \le r_1 < 10$. If $q_1 = 0$, $a = 10r_1 + r_0$, and the symbol for a is r_1r_0. If $q_1 > 0$, $q_1 = 10q_2 + r_2$, $0 \le r_2 < 10$. If $q_2 = 0$, $a = 10(10r_2 + r_1) + r_0 = 10^2r_2 + 10r_1 + r_0$, and the symbol for a is $r_2r_1r_0$. If $q_2 > 0$, the process is repeated. Since the q_i form a decreasing set of nonnegative integers, the process must cease in a finite number of steps.   Thus

$$a = 10^n r_n + 10^{n-1} r_{n-1} + \cdots + 10 r_1 + r_0,$$

and the symbol for a is $r_n r_{n-1} \cdots r_1 r_0$.   This representation is unique, for at each stage the quotients and remainders are unique. Negative integers are obviously represented in the same way, but they are preceded by a minus sign.

It is evident that the above process does not depend upon the particular integer 10, called the base.   Any other positive integer n can be used as a base, and the integer a can be represented by a sequence of the $n - 1$ symbols representing the $n - 1$ remainders modulo n.   For example, the base 3 might be used, and an integer can then be represented by means of the symbols 0, 1, 2. Since 15 can be written as $1 \cdot 3^2 + 2 \cdot 3 + 0$, its symbol written with the base 3 is 120.   The rules for addition and multiplication hold, but, of course, new tables must be learned if the computations are to be carried out with dispatch.   The addition and multiplication tables for the base 3 are:

+	0	1	2
0	0	1	2
1	1	2	10
2	2	10	11

×	0	1	2
0	0	0	0
1	0	1	2
2	0	2	11

Example.   Let 120 and 121 be integers written with the base 3. Find their sum and product.

sum

$$120 = 1 \cdot 3^2 + 2 \cdot 3 + 0$$
$$121 = 1 \cdot 3^2 + 2 \cdot 3 + 1$$
$$1011 = 2 \cdot 3^2 + 4 \cdot 3 + 1 = 3 \cdot 3^2 + 1 \cdot 3 + 1$$
$$= 1 \cdot 3^3 + 0 \cdot 3^2 + 1 \cdot 3 + 1$$

product

$$120 = 1 \cdot 3^2 + 2 \cdot 3 + 0$$
$$121 = 1 \cdot 3^2 + 2 \cdot 3 + 1$$

120	$1 \cdot 3^2 + 2 \cdot 3 \quad + 0$	$=$	$1 \cdot 3^2 + 2 \cdot 3 + 0$
1010	$2 \cdot 3^3 + 4 \cdot 3^2 + 0 \cdot 3$	$= 1 \cdot 3^4 + 0 \cdot 3^3 + 1 \cdot 3^2 + 0 \cdot 3$
120	$1 \cdot 3^4 + 2 \cdot 3^3 + 0 \cdot 3^2$	$= 1 \cdot 3^4 + 2 \cdot 3^3 + 0 \cdot 3^2$
22,220 $=$		$2 \cdot 3^4 + 2 \cdot 3^3 + 2 \cdot 3^2 + 2 \cdot 3 + 0$

Exercises

1. Find the symbol for 26 using in turn the base 2, 3, 4, 5, 9, and 12.

2. What number is represented by the symbol 333 if it is interpreted as a number written with the base 4, 5, or 9?

3. Make an addition and multiplication table for the base 5. Find the sum and product of 23 and 34 if these symbols represent numbers written with the base 5.

2

The Rational, Real, and Complex Numbers

1 · The rational numbers

It has been seen that the set of integers is not closed with respect to division. We shall now define the rational numbers and show that they obey the same laws that govern the integers and that the set of nonzero rational numbers is closed with respect to division. Just as we constructed the integers by using pairs of positive integers, we shall in a similar way construct the rational numbers by using pairs of integers. The pair of integers will be denoted by a/b, with $b \neq 0$.

Definition of equality. $a/b = c/d$ if and only if $ad = bc$. Note that this equality is not an identical equality, but it is a relation which is obviously reflexive and symmetric and is easily proved to be transitive. Hence it is an equivalence relation, and we can separate the pairs of integers into classes, putting into the same class all those pairs that are equal. A rational number is defined to be a class of equal pairs, and we shall represent a rational number by any pair of integers belonging to the class defining it.

We shall now examine these classes. Note that $ma/mb = a/b$, for all integers m not zero. Further, if the g.c.d. of a and b is m, so that $a = a_1 m$ and $b = b_1 m$, then $a/b = a_1/b_1$. Now if $(a, b) = 1$, the equality $a/b = c/d$ gives us $ad = bc$, and hence $c = ma$ and $d = mb$. Thus members of the same class are all of the form ma/mb, where m is any integer not zero. In practice we usually replace a/b, if $d = (a, b) > 1$, by its equal, a_1/b_1, where $a = a_1 d$ and $b = b_1 d$. Thus the class containing a/b may be represented by a_1/b_1, where $(a_1, b_1) = 1$.

Definition of addition. $\qquad a/b + c/d = (ad + bc)/(bd)$.

Definition of multiplication. $\quad (a/b)(c/d) = (ac)/(bd)$.

25

From our previous discussion we see that the addition and multiplication of pairs really define an addition and multiplication of classes of pairs, for if each pair is replaced by a pair equal to it we obtain a pair that belongs to the class of the sum or the product. Hence the sum and product of rational numbers has been defined.

It is easily verified by using the above definitions that the rational numbers obey the commutative and associative laws for both addition and multiplication and also the distributive law. For example, the distributive law,

$$\frac{a}{b}\left(\frac{c}{d} + \frac{e}{f}\right) = \frac{a}{b} \cdot \frac{c}{d} + \frac{a}{b} \cdot \frac{e}{f},$$

can be verified as follows:

$$\frac{a}{b}\left(\frac{c}{d} + \frac{e}{f}\right) = \frac{a}{b}\left(\frac{cf + de}{df}\right) = \frac{acf + ade}{bdf}$$

and

$$\frac{a}{b} \cdot \frac{c}{d} + \frac{a}{b} \cdot \frac{e}{f} = \frac{ac}{bd} + \frac{ae}{bf}$$

$$= \frac{acbf + aebd}{b^2 df}$$

$$= \frac{acf + aed}{bdf}.$$

Identity for addition. Since $a/b + 0/1 = a/b$ for every a/b, we say that $0/1$ is an identity for addition.

Additive inverse. Since $a/b + (-a)/b = (ab - ab)/b^2 = 0/1$, we say that $(-a)/b$ is an additive inverse of a/b.

Identity for multiplication. Since $(a/b)(c/c) = a/b$, we say that c/c is an identity for multiplication.

Cancellation laws for addition and multiplication. The student can verify that the cancellation laws for addition and multiplication hold; i.e., 1) if $a/b + c/d = a/b + e/f$, then $c/d = e/f$, and 2) if $(a/b)(c/d) = (a/b)(e/f)$, $a/b \neq 0/1$, then $c/d = e/f$.

Division. A pair a/b is divisible by c/d if a pair x/y exists such that $a/b = (x/y)(c/d)$. It is easily seen that $(ad)/(bc)$ is such a pair unless $c = 0$. If $c = 0$, then $a = 0$, and x/y is any pair. Thus any rational number is divisible by any nonzero rational number, and the set of nonzero rational numbers is closed under the so-called rational operations addition, subtraction, multiplication, and division.

2 · The integers as a subset of the rational numbers

We shall show that the subset of classes of pairs consisting of those classes of pairs which are of the form $a/1$ is isomorphic to the integers. A one-to-one correspondence can be set up as follows: Let the class represented by $a/1$ correspond to the integer a, and conversely let the integer a correspond to this class. Now if

$$\frac{a}{1} \leftrightarrow a \quad \text{and} \quad \frac{b}{1} \leftrightarrow b,$$

then

$$\frac{a}{1} + \frac{b}{1} = \frac{a + b}{1} \leftrightarrow a + b \quad \text{and} \quad \frac{a}{1} \cdot \frac{b}{1} = \frac{ab}{1} \leftrightarrow ab.$$

Since addition and multiplication are preserved under this one-to-one correspondence, this subset of classes is isomorphic to the set of integers. Since abstractly these two sets of entirely different entities are alike, we use them as if they were identical, and in practice we replace the symbol for a rational number of this subset by the symbol for an integer.

3 · The real numbers

It is evident that the rational numbers are not sufficient to meet ordinary needs. For example, the hypotenuse x of a right triangle each of whose legs is of unit length cannot be represented by a rational number, for its square is 2. If a rational number p/q, with $(p, q) = 1$, existed such that $p^2/q^2 = 2$, then $p^2 = 2q^2$, but we have seen (Exercise 5, p. 17) that such an equation has no solution in integers. To meet such obvious needs the real numbers are constructed from the rational numbers. No postulational approach to the real numbers will be given, and no proofs will be given that the real numbers obey the same laws of algebra that the rational numbers do. We shall merely describe how to obtain sequences of rational numbers that are approximations to the real numbers.

We need to recall the meaning of the decimal notation for

rational numbers. The number 3.12, for example, means

$$3 + \frac{1}{10} + \frac{2}{10^2}.$$

In general the sequence of integers $b.a_1a_2 \cdots a_n$, where $a_1, a_2, \cdots, a_n$ are remainders modulo 10, means

$$b + \frac{a_1}{10} + \frac{a_2}{10^2} + \cdots + \frac{a_n}{10^n},$$

whereas the notation $b.a_1a_2 \cdots a_n \cdots$ means that the decimal does not consist of a finite sequence of digits. Now any rational number can be converted into a decimal. For example, $32/5 = 6.4$. By the division algorithm we have $32 = 6(5) + 2$, and so 6 is the integral part of the decimal representation. Now multiply the remainder by 10, and we have $20 = 5(4)$. Four is therefore the first and final digit after the decimal point. Similarly we find that $1/7$ can be represented by the infinite repeating decimal $0.142857142857 \cdots$.

To convert any rational number c/d into a decimal we proceed in the same way. For convenience assume c and d positive. We have $c = db + r_0$, where $0 < r_0 < d$, and b is the integral part of c/d. Then $10r_0 = da_1 + r_1$, where $0 \le r_1 < d$. Since $r_0 < d$, $10r_0 = da_1 + r_1 < 10d$, and hence $a_1 < 10$. Thus a_1 is the first digit after the decimal point. If $r_1 = 0$, $c/d = b + a_1/10 = b.a_1$; but if $r_1 \ne 0$, we continue, obtaining $10r_1 = a_2d + r_2$, where $0 \le r_2 < d$. Thus $c/d = b + a_1/10 + a_2/10^2 + r_2/10^2d$. If $r_2 \ne 0$, we have a decimal approximation $b.a_1a_2$ to c/d; but if $r_2 = 0$, we have an exact representation of c/d as a finite decimal. Thus we may continue in this fashion obtaining any desired accuracy. If the rational number is not represented by a finite decimal, it is easily seen that the digits in the decimal part must repeat, for there are a finite number of remainders modulo d. It can also be proved that any infinite repeating decimal represents a rational number.

To return to the problem of constructing a number x to represent the hypotenuse of the above right triangle, we proceed as follows: We approximate to x, which as usual we shall denote by $\sqrt{2}$, by rational numbers, and we shall use the decimal notation. Now 2 lies between 1^2 and 2^2 and therefore between two consecutive terms of the sequence

$$(1.0)^2, \ (1.1)^2, \ (1.2)^2, \cdots, \ (1.9)^2, \ 2^2.$$

We find $(1.4)^2 < 2 < (1.5)^2$. Thus 2 lies between two consecutive terms of the sequence

$$(1.40)^2, \ (1.41)^2, \ (1.42)^2, \cdots, \ (1.49)^2, \ (1.50)^2,$$

and we find that $(1.41)^2 < 2 < (1.42)^2$. We may continue this process as long as we please, obtaining an approximation to $\sqrt{2}$ by means of decimals to any degree of accuracy desired. We say that $\sqrt{2}$ is represented by the infinite decimal $1.4142\cdots$.

The real numbers may be said to consist of the finite and infinite decimals, and we shall now interpret this definition geometrically. Represent the integers by points on a line as follows: Take two arbitrary points, labeling one 0 and the other 1. The distance between these two points is taken as the unit length, and we lay off unit intervals on the line labeling the points in the customary manner:

-3	-2	-1	0	1	2	3	4

The rational numbers, as we learn from elementary geometry, can also be laid off as points on this line. However, the rational numbers do not exhaust the points on the line, for we can lay off the hypotenuse of a right triangle whose legs are of unit length, and as we have seen this point cannot be represented by a rational number. Since there are numbers other than rational numbers which can be represented by points on the line, we extend our number system to include these numbers, and we assume that there is a one-to-one correspondence between the real numbers and the points on a line. The points that do not correspond to rational numbers, we say, correspond to irrational numbers, and our system of real numbers consists of the rational and irrational numbers.

It remains to show that to each point on the line there corresponds a uniquely determined decimal, finite or infinite. We do this in the following way. Let P be any point on the line. If it lies between two integral points i and $i + 1$, we say that it belongs to this interval. On the other hand, if it lies on a division mark i, it belongs to both intervals $(i - 1, i)$ and $(i, i + 1)$. We shall say arbitrarily that it belongs to the right-hand interval $(i, i + 1)$, and, in the further divisions that we shall make, we shall also take the right-hand interval if the point P lies on a division mark. Now let P belong to the interval $(i, i + 1)$. Divide this interval into ten equal parts by the points of division $i + 1/10$, $i + 2/10$, $\cdots$, $i + 9/10$, and label these subintervals 0, 1, 2, $\cdots$, 9 from left to right. The subinterval a_1 then has the end points $i + a_1/10$ and $i + (a_1 + 1)/10$. Let P belong to this subinterval. Divide this subinterval again into ten equal parts and say that P belongs to the new subinterval a_2, where a_2 is one of the integers 0, 1, 2, $\cdots$, 9. Then P belongs to the subinterval whose end points are

$$i + \frac{a_1}{10} + \frac{a_2}{10^2} \quad \text{and} \quad i + \frac{a_1}{10} + \frac{a_2 + 1}{10^2}.$$

If we continue this process t times, P will belong to the subinterval whose end points are

$$i + \frac{a_1}{10} + \frac{a_2}{10^2} + \cdots + \frac{a_t}{10^t}$$

and

$$i + \frac{a_1}{10} + \frac{a_2}{10^2} + \cdots + \frac{a_t + 1}{10^t}.$$

Now, of course, these end points may be written as $i.a_1a_2 \cdots a_t$ and $i.a_1a_2 \cdots a_t + 1/10^t$. We say that $i.a_1a_2 \cdots a_t$ is an approximation to the number representing P. If this process is continued indefinitely, we obtain the infinite decimal $i.a_1a_2 \cdots a_t \cdots$, which we say is the real number corresponding to P.

In our method of finding a decimal representation of P, we arbitrarily chose the right-hand interval in each case. We could, of course, have chosen the left-hand interval. This accounts for the two representations, for example, of 2, namely $2.0000 \cdots$ and $1.999 \cdots$.

It is evident that we need not have chosen the base 10 in our representation. For example, we could have divided each interval into five equal parts. Thus, if we had chosen the base 5, the positional representation of $1/3$ would have been $0.1313 \cdots$, meaning $1/5 + 3/5^2 + 1/5^3 + 3/5^4 + \cdots$.

Exercises

1. Prove that $\sqrt{3}$ is an irrational number.

2. Find a decimal approximation to $\sqrt{7}$ to three decimal places by the method used to find an approximation to $\sqrt{2}$.

3. Write $\frac{2}{3}$ with the base 5 and with the base 6.
4. Write 0.425 with the base 7.
5. Write 0.312 with the base 9.

4 · The complex numbers

The equation $x^2 + 2 = 0$ has no solution x that is a real number, for the square of every real number is positive or zero. The desire to have solutions for such equations led to the further extension of the number system, namely the complex numbers. We shall define the complex numbers in terms of the real numbers.

Definition. A complex number is an ordered pair of real numbers denoted by (a, b).

Definition of equality. Two complex numbers (a, b) and (c, d) are equal if and only if $a = c$ and $b = d$. Note that this is an identical equality.

Definition of addition. $(a, b) + (c, d) = (a + c, b + d)$.

Definition of multiplication. $(a, b) \cdot (c, d) = (ac - bd, ad + bc)$.

It will be left to the student to verify that the complex numbers obey the commutative, associative, and distributive laws.

Identity for addition.   Since $(a, b) + (0, 0) = (a, b)$, the identity for addition or the zero element is $(0, 0)$.

Additive inverse.   Since $(a, b) + (-a, -b) = (0, 0)$, we have $(-a, -b)$ as the additive inverse of (a, b). We define $-(a, b) = (-a, -b)$ and $(a, b) - (c, d) = (a, b) + (-c, -d)$.

Identity for multiplication.   Since $(a, b) \cdot (1, 0) = (a, b)$, $(1, 0)$ is the unity element or the identity for multiplication.

Cancellation laws.   The cancellation law for addition is readily proved from the definitions of equality and sum. The cancellation law for multiplication may be put into the more easily proved equivalent form $(a, b) \cdot (c, d) = (0, 0)$ implies $(a, b) = (0, 0)$ or $(c, d) = (0, 0)$. To prove this law, suppose $(c, d) \neq (0, 0)$. Then we have $(ac - bd, ad + bc) = (0, 0)$. Hence $ac - bd = 0$, $ad + bc = 0$, and hence $b(c^2 + d^2) = 0$. Thus $b = 0$, and $a = 0$. The student should prove that the two forms of the cancellation law for multiplication are equivalent.

Division.   It is easy to show that the solution (x, y) of the equation $(a, b) = (x, y) \cdot (c, d)$, where $(c, d) \neq (0, 0)$, is given by $x = (ac + bd)/(c^2 + d^2)$ and $y = (bc - ad)/(c^2 + d^2)$. Thus we find that division except by zero is always possible and that the set of nonzero complex numbers is closed under the rational operations.

5 · The real numbers as a subset of the complex numbers

We may set up an isomorphism between the subset of complex numbers $(a, 0)$ and the real numbers a as follows: Let

$$(a, 0) \leftrightarrow a \quad \text{and} \quad (b, 0) \leftrightarrow b,$$

then

$$(a, 0) + (b, 0) = (a + b, 0) \leftrightarrow a + b$$

and

$$(a, 0) \cdot (b, 0) = (ab, 0) \leftrightarrow ab.$$

In practice we disregard the fact that we have only an isomorphism between the real numbers and the complex numbers $(a, 0)$ and use the symbol for a real number when we are using any member of the subset $(a, 0)$.

Exercise

Show that the subset of complex numbers $(0, a)$ is not isomorphic to the real numbers.

6 · The notation $a + bi$

We shall now introduce the most common notation for the complex number (a, b), namely $a + bi$. Let the complex number $(0, 1)$ be denoted by i. Then $i^2 = (0, 1) \cdot (0, 1) = (-1, 0)$, a real number. Further, $(a, 0) \cdot (0, 1) = (0, a)$, and $(a, b) = (a, 0) + (0, b) = (a, 0) + (0, 1) \cdot (b, 0)$. Thus if we replace the complex numbers that correspond to real numbers by the usual single symbols for real numbers and replace the complex number $(0, 1)$ by i, we see that (a, b) can be written $a + bi$. When we use the notation $a + bi$, we carry out addition and multiplication as usual but replace i^2, where it occurs, by -1. We thus have an isomorphism between these two ways of writing a complex number, for if $(a, b) \leftrightarrow a + bi$ and if $(c, d) \leftrightarrow c + di$, then

$$(a, b) + (c, d) = (a + c, b + d) \leftrightarrow (a + c) + (b + d)i,$$

and

$$(a, b) \cdot (c, d) = (ac - bd, ad + bc) \leftrightarrow (ac - bd) + (ad + bc)i.$$

From now on we shall use the customary notation $a + bi$, in which

a and b are real numbers, for a complex number. If $b = 0$, we say that the number $a + 0i$, or simply a, is a real number. If $a = 0$ and if $b \neq 0$, the complex number is called a pure imaginary number.

The complex number $a - bi$ is called the *conjugate* of the complex number $a + bi$, and we note that $(a - bi)(a + bi) = a^2 + b^2$ is a nonnegative real number. We can easily express the quotient $(a + bi)/(c + di)$ as a complex number by multiplying numerator and denominator by $c - di$, obtaining $(ac + bd)/(c^2 + d^2) + i(bc - ad)/(c^2 + d^2)$.

Note: $\sqrt{-1}$ is also a symbol for i.

Exercises

1. Write the following numbers in the form $a + bi$: $1 - 2\sqrt{-2}$, $1/i$, $1/(1 + i)$, $(2 + 3i)/(1 + 4i)$, $(2 - \sqrt{-3})(3 + 2i)$, 2, i^3, i^4, i^{10}.

2. Show that $i^n = 1$, -1, i, $-i$ according as n is an integer congruent to 0, 2, 1, or 3 modulo 4.

7 · Geometric representation of complex numbers

Complex numbers may be represented by points in a plane. Let (x, y) be the rectangular cartesian coordinates of a point P in the plane. We say that the point P represents the complex number $x + iy$. Thus to each point in the plane we can attach a complex number, and every complex number represents a point in the plane. It is evident that real numbers correspond to the points on the x-axis and that pure imaginary numbers correspond to points on the y-axis. For this reason the x-axis is often called the axis of reals, and the y-axis the axis of imaginaries.

It is also useful to use polar coordinates. Let (ρ, θ) be the polar coordinates of a point P whose rectangular coordinates are (x, y), and restrict ρ to a positive number or zero. We recall that $\rho = \sqrt{x^2 + y^2}$, $x = \rho \cos \theta$, $y = \rho \sin \theta$, and $\tan \theta = y/x$. Now ρ is called the *absolute value* or *modulus* of the complex number $x + iy$, and θ is called the *angle* or *amplitude*. For example, the absolute value of the complex number $1 - i$ is $\sqrt{2}$, and its angle is $315°$. Hence $1 - i = \sqrt{2}(\cos 315° + i \sin 315°)$. In the general case $x + iy = \rho (\cos \theta + i \sin \theta)$, where ρ is the absolute value and θ is the angle.

The student must not fall into the error of reading off the angle or the absolute value of a complex number incorrectly when he encounters an expression that is similar to the standard form of a complex number written in polar coordinates.   For example, the angle of the complex number $2(\sin 30° + i \cos 30°)$ is not 30° but 60°, for this number must be written as $2[\cos(90°-30°)+i \sin(90°-30°)]$ in order to be in standard form.   Again $-2(\cos 60° + i \sin 60°)$ has 2 as its absolute value but 240° as its angle, for

$$-2(\cos\ 60°+i\ \sin\ 60°) = 2[\cos\ (180°+60°)+i\ \sin\ (180°+60°)].$$

In the representation of a complex number in polar coordinates, we note that, although the absolute value is uniquely determined, the angle is determined only to within integral multiples of 2π. Hence *two complex numbers are equal if and only if their absolute values are equal and if their angles differ by multiples of 2π.*   It is also useful to note that the conjugate of the number $\rho(\cos\theta+i\sin\theta)$ is $\rho[\cos\ (-\theta) + i\sin\ (-\theta)] = \rho(\cos\theta - i\sin\theta)$.

Exercises

1. Plot the following complex numbers: $2 + 2i$, $-1 - i$, -2, $2i$, $(1 + i)/(1 - i)$, $(2 - 2i)/i$.

2. Find the angle and absolute value of each of the following numbers: $3(\cos\ 20° + i\ \sin\ 20°)$, $-3(\cos\ 20° + i\ \sin\ 20°)$, $3(\sin\ 20° + i\ \sin\ 20°)$, $3(\sin\ 20° + i\cos\ 20°)$, $2(\cos\ 60° - i\sin\ 60°)$, $2(-\cos\ 60° + i\sin\ 60°)$.

3. Find the angle and absolute value of each of the numbers in Exercise 1 and the numbers $-1 + \sqrt{3}\,i$ and $i/(-1 - \sqrt{3}\,i)$.   Write these numbers in polar form.

8 · De Moivre's theorem

The product and quotient of two complex numbers when written in polar form give us some interesting results.   Let

$$z_1 = \rho_1(\cos\theta_1 + i\sin\theta_1) \quad \text{and} \quad z_2 = \rho_2(\cos\theta_2 + i\sin\theta_2).$$

Then

$$z_1 z_2 = \rho_1\rho_2[\cos\theta_1\cos\theta_2 - \sin\theta_1\sin\theta_2 + i(\sin\theta_1\cos\theta_2 + \cos\theta_1\sin\theta_2)]$$
$$= \rho_1\rho_2[\cos\ (\theta_1 + \theta_2) + i\sin\ (\theta_1 + \theta_2)].$$

Similarly

$$\frac{z_1}{z_2} = \frac{\rho_1(\cos \theta_1 + i \sin \theta_1)}{\rho_2(\cos \theta_2 + i \sin \theta_2)} \cdot \frac{(\cos \theta_2 - i \sin \theta_2)}{(\cos \theta_2 - i \sin \theta_2)}$$

$$= \frac{\rho_1}{\rho_2} [\cos (\theta_1 - \theta_2) + i \sin (\theta_1 - \theta_2)].$$

Thus we have the following theorem.

Theorem 1. The absolute value of the product of two complex numbers is the product of their absolute values, and the angle of the product is the sum of their angles. The absolute value of the quotient of two complex numbers is the quotient of their absolute values, and the angle of the quotient is the angle of the numerator minus the angle of the denominator.

Theorem 2. De Moivre's theorem. If n *is a positive integer*

$$[\rho(\cos \theta + i \sin \theta)]^n = \rho^n(\cos n\theta + i \sin n\theta).$$

This formula is an immediate extension of the formula for a product. It is left to the student to prove it by induction.

Exercises

1. Write $1/[\rho(\cos \theta + i \sin \theta)]$ in polar form.

2. Prove that $[\rho(\cos \theta + i \sin \theta)]^{-n} = \rho^{-n}[\cos (-n\theta) + i \sin (-n\theta)]$, where n is a positive integer.

3. What is the geometric locus of a complex number a) of fixed absolute value, b) of fixed angle?

4. Find the polar form of AB, A/B, A^2/B, and $1/A$, if $A = 2(\cos 30° + i \sin 30°)$ and $B = 4(\cos 50° + i \sin 50°)$.

5. Write the numbers $A = \sqrt{3} - i$, $B = -\sqrt{3} - i$, $C = -\sqrt{3} + i$ in polar form. Find the angle and absolute value of each of the following: A^3, B^2/AC.

6. Find the value of $(1 + i)^6$ by first writing $1 + i$ in polar form and then applying De Moivre's theorem. Write your final answer in the form $a + bi$. Similarly calculate $(1 - \sqrt{3}i)^5$.

7. Since $(\cos \theta + i \sin \theta)^3 = \cos 3\theta + i \sin 3\theta$, use the binomial theorem to find the value of $\cos 3\theta$ and $\sin 3\theta$ as functions of θ.

9 · The *n* nth roots of a complex number

We seek the solutions z of the equation $z^n = A$, where n is a positive integer and A a complex number. This problem is easily solved by using polar coordinates. Let $z = \rho(\cos \theta + i \sin \theta)$ and

$A = r(\cos \varphi + i \sin \varphi)$. Then $z^n = A$ becomes

$$\rho^n (\cos n\theta + i \sin n\theta) = r(\cos \varphi + i \sin \varphi).$$

Recalling that two complex numbers are equal if and only if their absolute values are equal and their angles differ by integral multiples of 2π, we have $\rho^n = r$ and $n\theta = \varphi + 2k\pi$, k being an integer. Hence $\rho = r^{1/n}$, the positive real nth root of r, and $\theta = \varphi/n + 2k\pi/n$. There will be as many different values of z as there are angles $\varphi/n + 2k\pi/n$, which are not coterminal. It is easily seen that these angles are not coterminal for the values $k = 0$, 1, $2, \cdots, (n - 1)$, for the difference of any two of them is less than 2π. For k any integer, write $k = nq + m$, with $0 \leq m < n$, and we see that the angle $\varphi/n + 2k\pi/n$ is coterminal with the angle $\varphi/n + 2m\pi/n$. Thus there are exactly n distinct values of z given by

$$r^{1/n}[\cos (\varphi/n + 2k\pi/n) + i \sin (\varphi/n + 2k\pi/n)],$$
$$k = 0, 1, 2, \cdots, (n - 1).$$

Hence there are exactly n nth roots of a complex number.

Example 1. Find the three cube roots of $8i$.

Write $8i = 8(\cos \pi/2 + i \sin \pi/2)$. Let $\rho(\cos \theta + i \sin \theta)$ be a cube root. Then $\rho^3(\cos 3\theta + i \sin 3\theta) = 8(\cos \pi/2 + i \sin \pi/2)$, and $\rho^3 = 8$ and $3\theta = \pi/2 + 2k\pi$. Hence $\rho = 2$, and $\theta = \pi/6 + 2k\pi/3$. The three cube roots of $8i$ are:

$$2 \left(\cos \frac{\pi}{6} + i \sin \frac{\pi}{6} \right) = \sqrt{3} + i,$$

$$2 \left(\cos \frac{5\pi}{6} + i \sin \frac{5\pi}{6} \right) = -\sqrt{3} + i,$$

$$2 \left(\cos \frac{3\pi}{2} + i \sin \frac{3\pi}{2} \right) = -2i.$$

Example 2. Find the n nth roots of 1.

These roots are often called the n nth roots of unity. Using the notation introduced above, we have $r = 1$, and $\varphi = 0$, and hence $\rho = 1$, and $\theta = 2k\pi/n$. Thus the n nth roots of unity are given by $\cos 2k\pi/n + i \sin 2k\pi/n$, $k = 0, 1, \cdots, (n - 1)$. Note that by De Moivre's theorem, if we let $R = \cos 2\pi/n + i \sin 2\pi/n$, the n nth roots of unity can be written $R, R^2, R^3, \cdots, R^n$.

Exercises

1. Find the three cube roots of 8 and simplify the answers.
2. Find the three cube roots of 1 and simplify the answers.
3. Find the four fourth roots of 1 and write them in simplified form. Which of these are square roots of 1?
4. Find the six sixth roots of 1. Which of these are square roots of 1, which are cube roots of 1?
5. Find the three cube roots of -8.
6. Find the two square roots of $(1 + i)/\sqrt{2}$.
7. Find the four fourth roots of $-16i$.

10 · Primitive nth roots of unity

In Example 2 above we showed that there are exactly n complex numbers whose nth powers are 1, namely the numbers $R = \cos 2\pi/n + i \sin 2\pi/n, R^2, R^3, \cdots, R^n = 1$. In the above exercises we noted that some of the fourth roots of 1 were also square roots of 1 and that the sixth roots of 1 contained square roots and cube roots of 1. It is of interest to investigate these matters more closely.

Primitive nth roots of unity. An nth root z of 1 is a primitive nth root of 1 if $z^n = 1$ and if $z^m \neq 1$, when $0 < m < n$.

Theorem 3. Let $R = \cos 2\pi/n + i \sin 2\pi/n$. *If* $(k, n) = d$, *then* R^k *is a primitive* n/dth *root of unity.*

Let $k = k_1 d$ and $n = n_1 d$ so that $(k_1, n_1) = 1$. Then $R^k = \cos 2k_1 d\pi/n_1 d + i \sin 2k_1 d\pi/n_1 d = \cos 2k_1\pi/n_1 + i \sin 2k_1\pi/n_1$. Now R^k is an $n_1 = n/d$th root of unity, for $(R^k)^{n_1} = \cos 2k_1\pi + i \sin 2k_1\pi$. Moreover, R^k is a primitive n/dth root of unity, for if $(R^k)^m = 1 = \cos 2k_1 m\pi/n_1 + i \sin 2k_1 m\pi/n_1, k_1 m/n_1$ is an integer. Since $(n_1, k_1) = 1$, n_1 divides m, but the least positive multiple of n_1 is n_1 itself.

Corollary 1. Those and only those nth roots of unity $R, R^2, \cdots, R^n$ *are primitive nth roots of unity whose exponents are relatively prime to* n.

From the above theorem R^k is a primitive nth root of unity if and only if $d = 1$.

Corollary 2. If U *is any primitive nth root of unity and* $(k, n) = d$, *then* U^k *is a primitive n/dth root of unity.*

Now $U = R^t$, where $(t, n) = 1$. Hence $U^k = R^{tk}$ and $(tk, n) = d$. Thus we may apply the theorem to R^{tk}.

Corollary 3. *The n nth roots of unity include all the mth roots of unity if and only if m divides n.*

If m divides n, $n = mk$. Then by the theorem R^k is a primitive mth root of unity and hence all the mth roots of unity are included among the nth roots. On the other hand, if all the mth roots of unity are included among the nth roots, then the primitive mth root $\cos 2\pi/m + i \sin 2\pi/m = R^v$. By the theorem if $(v, n) = d$, R^v is a primitive n/dth root of unity. Hence $n/d = m$ and $n = md$.

Exercises

1. Find the primitive cube roots of 1.
2. Find the primitive 8th roots of 1.
3. Find the primitive 5th roots of 1.
4. Show that if p is a prime there are exactly $p - 1$ primitive pth roots of 1.
5. How many real nth roots of 1 are there?
6. How many real nth roots of a positive real number are there?
7. How many real nth roots of a negative real number are there?
8. How many primitive p^2th roots of 1 are there if p is a prime?
9. Find the twelve 12th roots of 1. Which of these are primitive square roots, primitive cube roots, primitive fourth roots, primitive sixth roots?
10. If $R = \cos 2\pi/7 + i \sin 2\pi/7$, express R^{-1}, R^{-3}, R^{-15}, as R^k, where $0 < k < 7$.
11. If $\omega = -1/2 + i \sqrt{3}/2$, find the value of $\omega^n + \omega^{-n}$ for all positive integers n.

3

Elementary Theory of Groups

1 · Definition

We shall now begin the study of some of the mathematical systems that belong primarily to the division of mathematics called algebra. In any mathematical system we have, first of all, a set S of elements that we shall denote by $a, b, c, \cdots$ and an equals or equivalence relation between pairs of elements. We have had several examples of such equals relations, namely, ordinary identical equality, the equality used to define integers, the equality used to define rational numbers, and the congruence of integers. In all the algebraic systems that we shall study we shall assume without further mention an equals relation between pairs of elements.

In addition to elements and an equivalence relation in an algebraic system, we have one or more operations on a pair of elements of the set S to produce a third element of S. Such operations are called binary operations. In general a binary operation o on a set of elements S is a rule that assigns to every ordered pair of elements a, b in S a unique element c in S, and we write $a \circ b = c$. The binary operation is well defined if, when either a or b or both a and b are replaced by elements respectively equal to them, c is replaced by an element equal to it. Familiar binary operations are those of addition and multiplication of numbers.

One of the simplest of all algebraic systems is that of a group. We give the following definition.

Postulates for a group. A set S of elements $a, b, c, \cdots$ forms a group with respect to the operation o if the following properties hold:

1) If a and b are in S, then $a \circ b$ is in S (closure).

2) For all a, b, c in S, $a \circ (b \circ c) = (a \circ b) \circ c$ (associative law).

3) There exists in S an element i, called a left-identity, such that $i \circ a = a$ for every a in S.

4) For each a in S, the equation $x \circ a = i$ has a solution x in S. The solution x is called a left-inverse of a and is denoted by a^{-1}.

The student should note that, while a left-identity i is the same for all elements a in S, a left-inverse of an element a is determined by the given element a. Although in the following examples and exercises all the group operations obey the commutative law, the student should not conclude that commutivity is demanded by the postulates. If $a \circ b = b \circ a$ for all a, b in the group, the group is called a *commutative* or *abelian* group. Examples of nonabelian groups will be encountered later.

Examples. The chief examples of groups that the student has encountered so far are found in the number system.

a) The integers form a group with respect to addition but not with respect to multiplication.

b) The residue classes modulo 3 form a group with respect to addition, and the nonzero residue classes modulo 3 form a group with respect to multiplication.

c) The numbers i, -1, $-i$, and 1 form a group with respect to multiplication.

Exercises

In each of the following exercises check through all the postulates for a group.

1. Do the even integers form a group with respect to addition? Do the odd integers form a group with respect to addition?

2. Do the positive real numbers form a group with respect to multiplication? Do all the rational numbers form a group with respect to multiplication?

3. Do the positive irrational numbers form a group with respect to multiplication?

4. Let $a \circ b = a - b$, where a and b are integers. Do the integers form a group with respect to this operation?

5. Prove that the nonzero residue classes modulo 5 form a group with respect to multiplication.

6. Prove that the nonzero residue classes modulo 4 do not form a group with respect to multiplication.

7. Show that all integers of the form $3m$, where m is an integer, form a group with respect to addition.

8. Show that all integral multiples of a fixed integer k form a group with respect to addition.

9. If the residue classes modulo 7 are denoted by the integers 0, 1, 2, 3, 4, 5, 6, which of the following sets form a group with respect to multiplication:
a) [1,2,4], b) [0,1,2,3,4,5,6], c) [1,6], d) [1,3,4,5], e) [1,2,3,4,5,6]?

⚮ 10. Show that the fifth roots of unity form a group with respect to multiplication.

⚮ 11. Show that the n nth roots of unity form a group with respect to multiplication.

⚮ 12. Show that the residue classes modulo m form a group with respect to addition.

⚮ 13. Show that the nonzero residue classes modulo p form a group with respect to multiplication if and only if p is a prime.

⚮ 14. Prove that the residue classes C_a modulo m such that $(a, m) = 1$ form a group with respect to multiplication.

2 · Elementary properties

We now prove some simple theorems directly from the definition of a group. In the theorems that follow ab will mean $a \circ b$, and the binary operation will be called multiplication.

Theorem 1. If a, b, c *are in a group,* ab = ac *implies* b = c.

Multiply the equation $ab = ac$ on the left by a left-inverse a^{-1} of a and apply the associative law, obtaining $(a^{-1}a)b = (a^{-1}a)c$, which gives us $ib = ic$ and finally $b = c$.

Theorem 2. In a group a left-identity element is also a right-identity element, i.e., ia = ai = a *for every* a *in the group.*

Let a^{-1} be a left-inverse of a. Then $a^{-1}(ai) = (a^{-1}a)i = ii = i = a^{-1}a$. Applying Theorem 1, we have $ai = a$. Henceforth we shall drop the qualifying words left and right and use the term identity for i.

Theorem 3. In a group a left-inverse a^{-1} *of an element* a *is also a right-inverse of* a, *i.e.,* $a^{-1}a = aa^{-1} = i$.

Now $a^{-1}(aa^{-1}) = (a^{-1}a)a^{-1} = ia^{-1} = a^{-1} = a^{-1}i$. Thus by Theorem 1, $aa^{-1} = i$. From now on we shall use the term inverse for a^{-1}.

Corollary. If a,b,c *are elements in a group, then* ba = ca *implies* b = c.

The proof is the same as for Theorem 1, for now we can multiply on the right by an inverse of a and obtain $b = c$.

Theorem 4. If a *and* b *are elements in a group, the equations* $ax = b$ *and* $ya = b$, *respectively, have unique solutions* x *and* y *in the group.*

We readily see that a solution of $ax = b$ is $a^{-1}b$ and that a solution of $ya = b$ is ba^{-1}, for $a(a^{-1}b) = (aa^{-1})b = ib = b$, and $(ba^{-1})a = b(a^{-1}a) = bi = b$. The solutions are unique, for, if x' and y' are second solutions, then $ax = ax'$ and $ya = y'a$, giving $x = x'$ and $y = y'$.

Corollary 1. The identity element in a group is unique.

The identity is the unique solution of the equation $ax = a$.

Corollary 2. The inverse of an element in a group is unique.

The inverse a^{-1} of a is the unique solution of the equation $ax = i$.

Corollary 3. The inverse of a^{-1} *is* a.

The element a is obviously the solution of the equation $a^{-1}x = i$. Hence we observe the following law of exponents $(a^{-1})^{-1} = a$.

Theorem 5. The inverse of a product is the product of the inverses in the reverse order; i.e., $(ab)^{-1} = b^{-1}a^{-1}$.

Now $(b^{-1}a^{-1})(ab) = b^{-1}(a^{-1}a)b = b^{-1}(ib) = b^{-1}b = i$.

3 · Permutations

So far all the binary operations we have encountered have obeyed the commutative law. We shall now define some symbols and find that the rule for combining them does not obey the commutative law.

The operation of replacing each of the n integers $1, 2, \cdots, n$ by one of them so that no two distinct integers are replaced by the same integer is called a permutation performed on the integers $1, 2, \cdots, n$. A permutation replaces any arrangement of the n integers by a new arrangement. It is obvious that the n integers merely form a convenient notation for any set of n symbols. We introduce a symbol for a permutation. Let $j_1, j_2, \cdots, j_n$ be any arrangement of the set of integers $1, 2, \cdots, n$. The symbol

$$p = \begin{pmatrix} 1 & 2 & 3 & \cdots & n \\ j_1 & j_2 & j_3 & \cdots & j_n \end{pmatrix}$$

shall mean replace 1 by j_1, replace 2 by j_2, and finally replace n by j_n. Such a symbol denotes a permutation. Note that the order of the columns in the symbol is immaterial.

We define the product of two permutations $p \circ q$ or, as we shall write it, pq as meaning first perform p and then perform q. Thus, if

$$q = \begin{pmatrix} j_1 & j_2 & \cdots & j_n \\ k_1 & k_2 & \cdots & k_n \end{pmatrix},$$

where $k_1, k_2, \cdots, k_n$ are $1, 2, \cdots, n$ in some order,

$$pq = \begin{pmatrix} 1 & 2 & 3 & \cdots & n \\ k_1 & k_2 & k_3 & \cdots & k_n \end{pmatrix}.$$

In general this multiplication is not commutative, for if, for example,

$$p = \begin{pmatrix} 1 & 2 & 3 \\ 3 & 1 & 2 \end{pmatrix} \quad \text{and} \quad q = \begin{pmatrix} 1 & 2 & 3 \\ 1 & 3 & 2 \end{pmatrix},$$

then

$$pq = \begin{pmatrix} 1 & 2 & 3 \\ 2 & 1 & 3 \end{pmatrix} \quad \text{and} \quad qp = \begin{pmatrix} 1 & 2 & 3 \\ 3 & 2 & 1 \end{pmatrix}.$$

However, we may prove that permutation multiplication is associative. Let p and q be the permutations on n symbols given above, and let

$$r = \begin{pmatrix} k_1 & k_2 & \cdots & k_n \\ m_1 & m_2 & \cdots & m_n \end{pmatrix},$$

where $m_1, m_2, \cdots, m_n$ are the integers $1, 2, \cdots, n$ in some order. Using the value of pq already found, we have

$$(pq)r = \begin{pmatrix} 1 & 2 & 3 & \cdots & n \\ m_1 & m_2 & m_3 & \cdots & m_n \end{pmatrix},$$

while

$$qr = \begin{pmatrix} j_1 & j_2 & \cdots & j_n \\ m_1 & m_2 & \cdots & m_n \end{pmatrix} \quad \text{and} \quad p(qr) = \begin{pmatrix} 1 & 2 & \cdots & n \\ m_1 & m_2 & \cdots & m_n \end{pmatrix}.$$

Thus $(pq)r = p(qr)$.

For every arrangement of 1, 2, 3, $\cdots$, n we may write down a different permutation. Since there are $n!$ different arrangements of n symbols, there are $n!$ different permutations on n symbols, which can be written down by inserting in the second row of p the $n!$ different arrangements of 1, 2, $\cdots$, n.

Theorem 6. *The* n! *permutations on* n *symbols form a group with respect to permutation multiplication.*

Since all the permutations on n symbols are included in the set, the set is closed with respect to permutation multiplication. This multiplication has just been proved to be associative. The identity is

$$i = \begin{pmatrix} 1 & 2 & 3 & \cdots & n \\ 1 & 2 & 3 & \cdots & n \end{pmatrix},$$

for it obviously has the property $ip = pi = p$ for any permutation p on the n integers 1, 2, $\cdots$, n. Let p be the permutation given above. Then the inverse of p is

$$p^{-1} = \begin{pmatrix} j_1 & j_2 & \cdots & j_n \\ 1 & 2 & \cdots & n \end{pmatrix},$$

for $pp^{-1} = p^{-1}p = i$.

This group is called the *symmetric group* on n symbols and plays an important role in many applications of group theory.

Cyclic notation. It is convenient to write permutations in what is called cyclic notation or in cycles. For example, the permutation

$$s = \begin{pmatrix} 1 & 2 & 3 & 4 \\ 2 & 3 & 4 & 1 \end{pmatrix}$$

may be written simply as (1234). We read the new symbol in cyclical order from left to right as follows: 1 is replaced by 2, 2 is replaced by 3, 3 is replaced by 4, and 4 is replaced by 1. Note that $(1234) = (2341) = (3412) = (4123)$. Again the permutation

$$t = \begin{pmatrix} 1 & 2 & 3 & 4 & 5 \\ 2 & 3 & 1 & 5 & 4 \end{pmatrix}$$

is written (123)(45), and the permutation

$$u = \begin{pmatrix} 1 & 2 & 3 \\ 1 & 3 & 2 \end{pmatrix}$$

is written either as $(1)(23)$ or simply as (23).   It is understood that when a symbol is omitted it is replaced by itself.   It is now reasonably clear that any permutation may be written as a product of cycles no two of which have a symbol in common.

Exercises

1. Write out the 4! permutations on 4 symbols in the two-rowed notation and in the cyclic notation.

2. Perform the following permutation multiplications: a) $(1245)(32154)$, b) $(123)(243)(134)$,   c) $(15624)(6321)$.

3. Find the inverse of each of the products in Exercise 2.

4. Perform the following permutation multiplications:

a) $(243)(13)$,   b) $(4312)(2341)$,   c) $(43)(3421)$,   d) $(431)(231)$,
e) $(12)(34)(24)$,   f) $(132)(1342)$,   g) $(34)(143)$,   h) $(1432)(14)$,
i) $(1324)(134)$,   j) $(1423)(24)$,   k) $(142)(23)$,   l) $(234)(143)$.

5. If $a = (123456)$, find a^2, a^3, a^4, a^5, a^6.

6. Show that the six permutations in Exercise 5 form a group with respect to permutation multiplication.

4 · Even and odd permutations

Definition.   A permutation that displaces only two symbols is called a transposition.

Theorem 7.   A cycle of n *symbols can be written as a product of* n − 1 *transpositions.*

This is clear when we exhibit the identity

$$(1234 \cdots n) = (12)(13)(14) \cdots (1n).$$

Hence any permutation can be written as a product of transpositions since each of its cycles can be so written.

A permutation can be written as a product of transpositions in many ways. For example, $(123) = (12)(13)$, and $(123) = (13)(12)(13)(12)$.   However, for a given permutation the number of transpositions is always even or always odd.   This we prove in the following theorem.

Theorem 8.   Let a permutation p *be written as a product of* a *transpositions and as a product of* b *transpositions.   Then* a ≡ b *(mod 2).*

In order to prove this theorem, consider the so-called alternating function A on the n distinct symbols $x_1, x_2, \cdots, x_n$, which is the product of the $n(n-1)/2$ factors $(x_i - x_j)$, $i < j$. Thus

$$A = \prod_{i<j}^{n} (x_i - x_j)$$
$$= (x_1 - x_2)(x_1 - x_3)(x_1 - x_4) \cdots (x_1 - x_n)$$
$$(x_2 - x_3)(x_2 - x_4) \cdots (x_2 - x_n)$$
$$(x_3 - x_4) \cdots (x_3 - x_n)$$
$$\cdots\cdots\cdots\cdots\cdots$$
$$(x_{n-1} - x_n).$$

Operate on A by the transposition $t = (x_i x_j)$, where $i < j$. Every factor of A that contains neither x_i nor x_j remains unchanged when A is operated on by the permutation t, but the factor $(x_i - x_j)$ of A is changed into its negative. The factors of A containing either x_i or x_j, but not both x_i and x_j, may be grouped into pairs of products $\pm (x_k - x_i)(x_k - x_j)$, where $k \neq i, j$. Such a product remains unchanged when it is operated on by t. Hence when A is operated on by a transposition t it becomes $-A$.

Now operate on A by the permutation p, which can be written as a product of a transpositions and as a product of b transpositions. Operating on A by p when it is written as a product of a transpositions, we obtain $(-1)^a A$, whereas, operating on A by p when it is written as a product of b transpositions, we obtain $(-1)^b A$. Because p is the same permutation no matter how it is written, $(-1)^a A = (-1)^b A$, which shows that $a \equiv b \pmod 2$.

Definition. A permutation is called an even permutation or an odd permutation according as it can be written as a product of an even number or an odd number of transpositions.

Theorem 9. Of the n! *permutations on* n *symbols* n!/2 *are even permutations and* n!/2 *are odd permutations.*

Of the $n!$ permutations on n symbols let $e_1, e_2, \cdots, e_s$ be the even permutations and $o_1, o_2, \cdots, o_t$ be the odd permutations. Multiply each of these permutations on the left by the transposition t. The te_j, $j = 1, 2, \cdots, s$, are odd permutations, for to each e_j has been added the one transposition t, whereas the to_k, $k = 1, 2, \cdots, r$, are even permutations, for to each o_k has been added the one transposition t. We now prove that the te_j and the to_k are the $n!$ permutations over again. Since even and odd permutations are distinct, we need prove only that no $te_v = te_w$ when

$e_v \neq e_w$, and no $to_v = to_w$ when $o_v \neq o_w$. This follows directly from the cancellation law, for $te_v = te_w$ implies $e_v = e_w$, and $to_v = to_w$ implies $o_v = o_w$. Thus the te_j, $j = 1, 2, \cdots, s$, are the permutations o_k, $k = 1, 2, \cdots, r$, in some order, and hence $s = r = n!/2$.

Exercises

1. Show that the identity is an even permutation.

2. Show that a cycle containing an odd number of symbols is an even permutation, whereas a cycle containing an even number of symbols is an odd permutation.

3. Write each of the 4! permutations on 4 symbols as a product of transpositions. Which are even permutations and which are odd permutations?

4. If p is an even permutation, show that p^{-1} is an even permutation.

5. Prove that the $n!/2$ even permutations on n symbols form a group with respect to permutation multiplication. This group is known as the *alternating group* on n symbols.

5 · Isomorphism

Definition. An isomorphism between two groups G and G' is a one-to-one correspondence $a \leftrightarrow a'$ between the elements a and a' of G and G' respectively such that, if $a \leftrightarrow a'$ and $b \leftrightarrow b'$, then $ab \leftrightarrow a'b'$. In the isomorphism, a' is called the image of a.

Note that an isomorphism does not demand that the operation or law of combination for the elements of each group be the same. We have omitted the symbol for the operation in the definition, but, if o is the operation for G and if o$'$ is the operation for G', then the condition for an isomorphism reads $a' \text{ o}' b' = (a \text{ o } b)'$.

Example. Let G be the multiplicative group on the fourth roots of unity, and let G' be the additive group of the residue classes modulo 4 whose elements will be denoted by 0, 1, 2, 3. Then we may set up an isomorphism between G and G' in the following two ways:

G		G'		G		G'
1	$\leftrightarrow$	0		1	$\leftrightarrow$	0
i	$\leftrightarrow$	1		i	$\leftrightarrow$	3
-1	$\leftrightarrow$	2		-1	$\leftrightarrow$	2
$-i$	$\leftrightarrow$	3;		$-i$	$\leftrightarrow$	1.

The number of ways an isomorphism can be established between two groups depends upon the structure of the group. No matter how the isomorphism is set up, however, we should observe the following fact. Write the so-called "mutiplication table" for each group G and G'.

G:

×	1	i	−1	−i
1	1	i	−1	−i
i	i	−1	−i	1
−1	−1	−i	1	i
−i	−i	1	i	−1

G':

+	0	1	2	3
0	0	1	2	3
1	1	2	3	0
2	2	3	0	1
3	3	0	1	2

For each isomorphism we see that the two multiplication tables become identical if each symbol of G is replaced by its image in G', and conversely.

Theorem 10. In an isomorphism between two groups G *and* G′ *whose elements are denoted by* a *and* a′ *respectively, the identities correspond, and, if* a′ *is the image of* a, *then the image of* a^{-1} *is* $(a')^{-1}$.

First prove that the identities correspond. Let i be the identity of G, and let i' be the identity of G'. Let $i \leftrightarrow a'$ and $x \leftrightarrow x'$, where x' is any element of G'. Then, since $ix = x$, we have from the isomorphism $a'x' = x'$ for any x' of G. Hence a' is an identity for G', and, since the identity is unique, $a' = i'$.

Next prove that inverse elements correspond. Let $a \leftrightarrow a'$ and $a^{-1} \leftrightarrow b'$. Since $a^{-1}a = i$, we have from the isomorphism $b'a' = i'$, and, since the inverse of an element is unique, $b' = (a')^{-1}$.

Exercises

1. Set up an isomorphism between the multiplicative group of the fourth roots of unity and the permutation group whose elements are $i = (1)(2)(3)(4)$, (1234), (13)(24), (1432).

2. Is it possible to set up an isomorphism between the multiplicative group of the fourth roots of unity and the permutation group whose elements are $i = (1)(2)(3)(4)$, (12)(34), (13)(24), (14)(23)?

3. Set up an isomorphism between the multiplicative group of the five fifth roots of unity and the permutation group whose elements are $i = (1)(2)(3)(4)(5)$, (12345), (13524), (14253), (15432).

6 · Cyclic groups

Integral powers of an element. We shall define integral powers of a group element a. By a^m, where m is a positive integer, we shall mean $a \circ a \circ \cdots \circ a$ to m factors. (If the operation is addition, we usually denote a^m by ma, where it is understood that m is not necessarily a group element and usually it is not.) Note that this writing of m factors without parentheses is possible only because a "product" of m factors is independent of the manner in which the factors are grouped. This generalized associative law can be proved by induction from the associative law. Further, we define $a^0 = i$, the identity, and $a^{-m} = (a^{-1})^m$, where m is a positive integer. With these definitions it is easy to prove the following theorem.

Theorem 11. For any element a *in a group,* 1) $a^r \circ a^s = a^{r+s}$, and 2) $(a^r)^s = a^{rs}$.

First we shall establish 1). For positive integral exponents this law is simply an application of the definition, for $a^r \circ a^s = a \circ a \circ \cdots \circ a$ to $r + s$ factors. From the definition of a^0, 1) holds if one or both exponents are zero. In case $r = -m$, $s = -n$, m and n positive integers, we have

$$a^r \circ a^s = a^{-m} \circ a^{-n} = (a^{-1})^m \circ (a^{-1})^n \quad \text{by definition,}$$
$$= (a^{-1})^{m+n} \quad \text{by 1) for positive exponents,}$$
$$= a^{-(m+n)} \quad \text{by definition,}$$
$$= a^{r+s}.$$

If $r = -m$ and if $s = n$, where m and n are positive integers, we have, using the definition of negative exponents,

$$a^r \circ a^s = a^{-m} \circ a^n = a^{-1} \circ a^{-1} \circ \cdots \circ a^{-1} \circ a \circ a \cdots \circ a$$

(m factors a^{-1} and n factors a),

$$= a^{n-m}, \quad m \leq n,$$
$$= (a^{-1})^{m-n}, \quad m > n,$$
$$= a^{-m+n} = a^{r+s}.$$

Thus all cases have been investigated and 1) holds for all integral exponents.

Now we shall establish 2). It is again obvious that 2) holds if either or both exponents are zero. If $s > 0$, then

$$(a^r)^s = a^r \circ a^r \circ \cdots \circ a^r \text{ to } s \text{ factors}$$
$$= a^{rs} \text{ by 1).}$$

If $s = -n$, where n is a positive integer, we have by definition

$$(a^r)^s = (a^r)^{-n} = [(a^r)^{-1}]^n.$$

Now $(a^r)^{-1}$ is the inverse of a^r and by 1) $a^r \circ a^{-r} = a^0$. Hence, since the inverse of an element is unique, $(a^r)^{-1} = a^{-r}$. Therefore

$$[(a^r)^{-1}]^n = (a^{-r})^n = a^{-rn} \text{ by 1)}$$
$$= a^{rs}.$$

Unless a and b are commutative, $(ab)^r \neq a^r b^r$, for $(ab)^r = (ab) \circ (ab) \circ \cdots \circ (ab)$, to r factors.

Definition of a cyclic group. Note that the above definitions of the integral powers of a group element a together with Theorem 11 prove that the integral powers of any group element a form a group. A group consisting only of the powers of a single element a is called a cyclic group. Such an element a is called a generator of the cyclic group.

Definition of the order of an element. An element a in a group is said to be of order n, if n is the least positive integer such that $a^n = i$, the identity. An element a is said to be of order zero if no positive power of a is the identity; i.e., a^0 is the only power of a which is the identity.

Order of a group. A group consisting of a finite number of elements is called a finite group, whereas a group having infinitely many elements is called an infinite group. The order of a finite group is the number of its elements. An infinite group is said to have the order zero.

Theorem 12. *If a generator* a *of a cyclic group* G *is of order zero,* G *is isomorphic to the additive group of integers. If a generator* a *of* G *is of order* n > 0, G *is isomorphic to the additive group of residue classes modulo* n.

We shall prove first that if the order of a is zero no two powers of a are equal. For, if $a^s = a^t$ when $s \neq t$, then $a^s a^{-t} = a^t a^{-t} = i$, and $a^{s-t} = i = a^{t-s}$, and thus, since either $s - t$ or $t - s$ is positive, a positive power of a equals i. Now, since $a^s a^t = a^{s+t}$, the correspondence $a^s \leftrightarrow s$ is an isomorphism, and G is isomorphic to the additive group of integers.

Now let a be of order $n > 0$, and we shall prove that G consists of only n distinct elements. For any integer s, we have $s = nq + r$, where $0 \leq r < n$. Thus any element a^s of G may be written

$a^s = a^{nq+r} = a^{nq}a^r = (a^n)^q a^r = ia^r = a^r.$ If $x > y$, where $0 < x < n$, and $0 \leq y < n$, then $a^x \neq a^y$, for, if $a^x = a^y$, $a^{x-y} = i$; but $0 < x - y < n$, contrary to the definition of the order of a. Hence there are exactly n distinct elements a, a^2, a^3, $\cdots$, a^{n-1}, $a^n = a^0 = i$ in the group. Denoting the residue classes modulo n by C_0, C_1, C_2, $\cdots$, C_{n-1}, we see that the correspondence $a^s \leftrightarrow C_s$ is an isomorphism between the additive group of residue classes modulo n and G, for, if $a^t \leftrightarrow C_t$, then $a^s a^t = a^{s+t} = a^r \leftrightarrow C_s + C_t = C_r$, where $s + t \equiv r \pmod{n}$.

Exercises

1. Show that the following permutations form a group: $i = (1)(2)(3)(4)$, (1234), $(13)(24)$, (1432), (13), (24), $(14)(23)$, $(12)(34)$. Is this group isomorphic to the multiplicative group of the eighth roots of unity? Is the permutation group a cyclic group? Is the multiplicative group of the eighth roots of unity a cyclic group?

2. In the following problems denote the residue classes modulo m by 0, 1, $2, \cdots, m - 1$.

    a) Is the multiplicative group 1, 2, 3, 4, 5, 6 modulo 7 cyclic?

    b) Is the multiplicative group 1, 3, 5, 7 modulo 8 cyclic?

    c) Is the multiplicative group 1, 2, 4, 5, 7, 8 modulo 9 cyclic?

3. Is the additive group of integral multiples of 5 cyclic?

4. Set up an isomorphism in as many ways as possible between the multiplicative group of the sixth roots of unity and the additive group of residue classes modulo 6.

5. How many elements of the cyclic group of order 6 can be used as generators of the group?

7 · Subgroups

Definitions. A subset S of elements of a group G that is itself a group is called a subgroup of G. The law of combination of the elements is understood to be the same as that for the group itself. The identity alone as well as the group G itself satisfies this definition. Subgroups other than the identity and the group itself are called *proper* subgroups, and we are chiefly interested in these.

Theorem 13. Necessary and sufficient conditions that a subset S of elements of a group G forms a group are 1) if a and b are in S, then ab is in S, and 2) if a is in S, then a^{-1} is in S.

Note that these conditions reduce the number of postulates to be tested from four to two. We prove first that if these conditions hold, the set S forms a group.   Conditions 1) and 2) ensure the closure of the set, the presence of the identity in S, and the presence of the inverse of each element a of S in S.   The associative law holds because the elements of S are in G.   Hence the postulates for a group are satisfied.   On the other hand, if the set S forms a group, 1) holds.   Now the identity of G is an identity for S. Since S is a group its identity is unique, and hence the identity of S is the identity of G.   Moreover, since the inverse of an element in G is unique, the inverse of an element a in S is also the inverse of a in G.   Hence 2) holds.

We shall now determine the subgroups of a cyclic group.

Theorem 14.   A subgroup S *of a cyclic group* G *is cyclic.   If* a *is a generator of* G, S *is generated by* a^{m}, *where* m *is the least positive integer such that* a^{m} *is in* S.   *If* G *is of order zero, the integer* m *is arbitrary and* S *is isomorphic to the additive group of integral multiples of* m.   *If* G *is of order* n > 0, m *divides* n *and* S *is of order* n/m.

Let a be a generator of G, and let S be a proper subgroup of G. Because S is a proper subgroup of G, it contains some element a^s other than the identity and its inverse a^{-s}.   Now either s or $-s$ is a positive integer.   Hence let m be the least positive integer such that a^m is in S.   If a^t is in S, write $t = mq + r$, with $0 \leq r < m$.   Now $(a^m)^q = a^{mq}$ is in S, and therefore $a^t a^{-mq} = a^{t-mq} = a^r$ is in S.   However, $r < m$.   Hence $r = 0$, and all elements in S are of the form a^{km}.   Thus a^m is a generator of S.   If a is of order zero, a^m is a generator of a subgroup for any integer m, and the correspondence $a^m \leftrightarrow m$ is an isomorphism between S and the additive group of integral multiples of m.   If a is of order $n > 0$, then $a^n = i$ is in S, and hence $n = mk$.   Thus a^m is of order $k = n/m$.

Exercises

1. Select cyclic subgroups of three different orders from the symmetric group on four symbols.

2. Exhibit the proper subgroups in the multiplicative group of the sixth roots of unity.

3. Exhibit the proper subgroups of the additive group of residue classes modulo 12.

4. Set up an isomorphism between the additive group of residue classes modulo 12 and the multiplicative group of the twelfth roots of unity.   What roots of unity correspond to the subgroups you have found in Exercise 3?

5. Find the elements of the additive group of residue classes modulo m which can be used as generators of the group.

6. Prove that the elements common to two subgroups S and T of a group G form a subgroup of G. This subgroup consisting of the elements common to S and T is called the *intersection* or *cross cut* of S and T.

7. Show that the following permutations form a group:

$i = (1)(2)(3)(4)(5)(6)(7)(8)$, $(1234)(5678)$, $(13)(24)(57)(68)$, $(1432)(5876)$, $(1537)(2846)$, $(1735)(2648)$, $(1836)(2745)$, $(1638)(2547)$.

Find three cyclic subgroups of order 4 of this group.

8. Show that in a group G those elements x such that $xa = ax$ for all a in G form a subgroup of G. This subgroup is called the *center* of G.

8 · Cosets and subgroups

We turn now to some properties of groups which will give us further insight into the structure of a group.

Definition. Let S be a subgroup of G, and let a be any element of G. The collection of elements Sa of G, which consists of the products of each element s of S by the element a of G, is called a right coset of S in G. Similarly, the collection of elements aS of G is called a left coset of S in G.

Note that according to this definition S itself is both a left coset and a right coset of S in G, for $iS = Si = S$. It is also of interest to point out that in an abelian group the right cosets and the left cosets of a subgroup S coincide, and in this case the qualifying adjectives right and left are omitted.

Example 1. Let G be the octic permutation group whose elements are $i = (1)(2)(3)(4)$, $a = (1234)$, $b = (13)(24)$, $c = (1432)$, $d = (13)$, $e = (24)$, $f = (12)(34)$, $g = (14)(32)$, and let S be the subgroup whose elements are i and $d = (13)$. Then the right cosets of S in G are S, Sa, Sc, Se, which respectively consist of the following sets of elements: i, (13); (1234), $(14)(32)$; (1432), $(12)(34)$; (24), $(13)(24)$.

Example 2. Let G be the additive group of integers, and let S be the subgroup of integral multiples of 3. In this case the cosets of S are the following sets of integers: $3m$, $3m + 1$, $3m + 2$.

We prove the following lemmas and theorems for right cosets, but it should be noted that similar statements and proofs can be made for left cosets.

Lemma 1. The set of elements Ss, *where* s *is any element of the group* S, *is the group* S.

We write $Ss = S$, meaning that the collection of elements Ss is identical except for order with the elements of S. The elements of the set Ss are in S, and any element s_k in S is in Ss, for $s_k = (s_k s^{-1})s$.

Lemma 2.   A one-to-one correspondence may be set up between the elements of a subgroup S and the elements of a right coset Sa of S in a group G.

The correspondence $s_i \leftrightarrow s_i a$ is one-to-one, for $s_i a = s_j a$ implies $s_i = s_j$.

Lemma 3.   Two right cosets Sa and Sb of a subgroup S in a group G either are identical or have no common elements.

Let x be an element common to Sa and Sb; i.e., $x = s_i a = s_j b$. Then $S(s_i a) = S(s_j b)$. However, $S(s_i a) = (Ss_i)a = Sa$ by Lemma 1, and similarly $S(s_j b) = Sb$.

Theorem 15.   The elements of a group G can be separated into mutually exclusive right cosets of a subgroup S in G.

Every element a of G belongs to some right coset of S in G, namely the right coset Sa, for this coset contains the element $ia = a$. By Lemma 3 a given element can belong to one and only one right coset of S. Thus we have separated the elements of G into mutually exclusive right cosets of S. We often speak of a as a representative of the right coset Sa.

Note that we really have introduced an equivalence relation between the elements of a group by the introduction of right cosets. For suppose that we say that two elements a and b of G are right congruent modulo the subgroup S if $b = sa$, where s is an element of S, and that we write $a \equiv b$ (mod S). Note $a \equiv a$, for $a = ia$. If $a \equiv b$, then $b \equiv a$, for if $b = sa$ then $a = s^{-1}b$. Moreover, if $a \equiv b$ and $b \equiv c$, then $a \equiv c$, for we have $b = sa$, $c = s'b$, and hence $c = s'(sa) = s''a$. It is also of interest to note that, if G is the additive group of integers and if S is the subgroup of integral multiples of a fixed integer m, the concept of the separation of G into cosets of the subgroup S is the same as the separation of the set of integers into residue classes modulo m. Stating that two integers a and b are congruent modulo m is the same as saying that they belong to the same residue class modulo m or the same coset of the subgroup S.

Theorem 16. *Theorem of Lagrange.* *The order of a subgroup S of a finite group G is a divisor of the order of G.*

Let g be the order of G and let s be the order of S. Separate the elements of G into right cosets of S, say k in number. By Lemma 2 each right coset contains the same number of elements. Hence $sk = g$.

Corollary 1. *The order of an element of a group of finite order divides the order of the group.*

The proof is immediate when we recall that any element of a group generates a cyclic subgroup of the group.

Corollary 2. *Every group of prime order* p *is cyclic.*

The order of the cyclic subgroup generated by an element $a \neq i$ must divide the prime p and hence is of order p itself. Thus the group consists of the powers of the element a.

Corollary 3. *Fermat's theorem.* *If* a *is an integer and* p *a prime, then* $a^p \equiv a \pmod{p}$.

The multiplicative group of nonzero residues modulo p, where p is a prime, is of order $p - 1$, and 1 is its identity. Thus, for any integer $a \not\equiv 0 \pmod{p}$, $a^{p-1} \equiv 1 \pmod{p}$, and hence $a^p \equiv a \pmod{p}$. The theorem is trivially true if $a \equiv 0 \pmod{p}$.

Exercises

1. Find the left cosets of the subgroup $i = (1)(2)(3)(4)$, $d = (13)$ of the octic permutation group. Are the left cosets the same as the right cosets found in Example 1?

2. Separate the elements of the symmetric group on four symbols into right cosets and also into left cosets of the octic group on four symbols.

3. Find all the subgroups of the octic permutation group.

4. Find all the subgroups of the symmetric group on three symbols.

5. Separate the elements of the symmetric group on four symbols into right and left cosets of the subgroup $i = (1)(2)(3)(4)$, $(12)(34)$, $(13)(24)$, $(14)(23)$.

6. Prove that a necessary and sufficient condition that two right cosets Sa and Sb of a subgroup S in a group G be identical is that ab^{-1} is an element of S.

7. What are the possible orders of the subgroups of the symmetric group on four symbols? Find examples of as many subgroups as you can.

9 · Cayley's theorem

To show the intimate relation between permutation groups and finite groups, we shall prove Cayley's theorem.

Theorem 17. Every finite group of order g is isomorphic to a permutation group on g symbols.

Let s_i, where $i = 1, 2, \cdots, g$, be the elements of the group G. Note that

$$\begin{pmatrix} s_i \\ s_i s_j \end{pmatrix}, \qquad i = 1, 2, \cdots, g,$$

is a permutation of the g elements of the group, for all the elements in the second row of the symbol are distinct. It is easy to show that these permutations form a group. Now, if we set up the one-to-one correspondence

$$s_j \leftrightarrow \begin{pmatrix} s_i \\ s_i s_j \end{pmatrix}, \quad s_k \leftrightarrow \begin{pmatrix} s_i \\ s_i s_k \end{pmatrix}, \qquad i = 1, 2, \cdots, g,$$

we have an isomorphism. For, if $s_j s_k = s_r$, then

$$s_r = s_j s_k \leftrightarrow \begin{pmatrix} s_i \\ (s_i s_j) s_k \end{pmatrix} = \begin{pmatrix} s_i \\ s_i (s_j s_k) \end{pmatrix}$$

$$= \begin{pmatrix} s_i \\ s_i s_r \end{pmatrix}, \qquad i = 1, 2, \cdots, g.$$

This permutation group is called a _regular permutation_ group. Each of its elements except the identity displaces g symbols.

Example. Find a regular permutation group isomorphic to the symmetric group on three symbols. Label the elements of the symmetric group on three symbols as follows: $s_1 = (1)(2)(3)$, $s_2 = (123)$, $s_3 = (132)$, $s_4 = (12)$, $s_5 = (13)$, $s_6 = (23)$. Then we can find the regular permutation representation from the following multiplication table. Note that we are multiplying each element of the group on the right by the element in the first column. We obtain another regular permutation group if we multiply on the left, but in that case we do not have the same isomorphism that was established in the theorem.

	s_1	s_2	s_3	s_4	s_5	s_6
s_1	s_1	s_2	s_3	s_4	s_5	s_6
s_2	s_2	s_3	s_1	s_5	s_6	s_4
s_3	s_3	s_1	s_2	s_6	s_4	s_5
s_4	s_4	s_6	s_5	s_1	s_3	s_2
s_5	s_5	s_4	s_6	s_2	s_1	s_3
s_6	s_6	s_5	s_4	s_3	s_2	s_1

regular permutation group

$(s_1)(s_2)(s_3)(s_4)(s_5)(s_6) = i$

$(s_1 s_2 s_3)(s_4 s_5 s_6)$

$(s_1 s_3 s_2)(s_4 s_6 s_5)$

$(s_1 s_4)(s_2 s_6)(s_3 s_5)$

$(s_1 s_5)(s_2 s_4)(s_3 s_6)$

$(s_1 s_6)(s_2 s_5)(s_3 s_4).$

A permutation of the regular permutation group replaces each element of the first row in the table by the element below it in any given row. The isomorphism is given by assigning the regular permutation on the right to its corresponding element of the group in the first column.

Exercises

Find a regular permutation group isomorphic to each of the following groups:
1. The cyclic group of order 5.
2. The cyclic group of order 6.
3. The octic group.

4

Rings, Integral Domains, and Fields

1 · Rings

We now turn to algebraic systems that deal with sets which are closed under two operations. The two operations will be called addition and multiplication, and we shall use the ordinary notation for these operations. However, it must be borne in mind that they may be not ordinary addition and multiplication but well-defined operations that satisfy the given postulates. The simplest of these systems is the ring.

Definition. A set of elements a, b, c, $\cdots$ forms a ring R with respect to the two operations addition and multiplication, if

 1) the set forms a commutative group with respect to addition;
 2) the set is closed with respect to multiplication;
 3) the associative law $a(bc) = (ab)c$ holds for multiplication;
 4) the distributive laws $a(b + c) = ab + ac$ and $(b + c)a = ba + ca$ hold.

Since the ring is a group with respect to addition, all the group properties for addition hold. The unique identity of the additive group is called the zero element of the ring, and we shall denote it by the ordinary symbol for the number zero. Thus $a + 0 = 0 + a = a$ for every a in the ring. We shall denote the unique additive inverse of an element a by $-a$, and we shall write $a + (-a) = a - a = 0$ and $a + (-b) = a - b$. Note that the properties of the additive inverse and the zero element give us the cancellation law, if $a + b = a + c$, then $b = c$; a unique solution $x = b - a$ of the equation $a + x = b$; and the rule $-(-a) = a$.

We can also prove $a \cdot 0 = 0$, for $a \cdot 0 + a \cdot a = a(0 + a) = a \cdot a = 0 + a \cdot a$, and hence by the above cancellation law for addition $a \cdot 0 = 0$. Similarly by using the right distributive law,

58

we can prove that $0 \cdot a = 0$. However, the converse that if a product $a \cdot b = 0$ one factor must be zero (the cancellation law for multiplication) need not necessarily hold, as we shall illustrate below.

A ring in which multiplication is commutative is called a *commutative* ring. We shall be interested primarily in commutative rings.

Examples. The student can check that the integers, the even integers, and the residue classes modulo m all form commutative rings with respect to addition and multiplication. These rings differ in certain ways. The ring of integers and the ring of residue classes have identity elements for multiplication, but the ring of even integers does not. Again, the cancellation law for multiplication holds in the ring of integers and in the ring of even integers, but does not hold in the ring of residue classes modulo m unless m is a prime number. If $m = ab$, i.e., if m is composite, we see that $ab \equiv 0 \pmod{m}$, but neither $a \equiv 0$ nor $b \equiv 0 \pmod{m}$. On the other hand, if $ab \equiv 0 \pmod{p}$, where p is a prime, we have either $a \equiv 0 \pmod{p}$ or $b \equiv 0 \pmod{p}$.

Divisors of zero. If $ab = 0$ and $a \neq 0$ and $b \neq 0$, then a and b are called proper divisors of zero. Thus we note that the ring of residue classes modulo m is a ring without proper divisors of zero if and only if m is a prime.

Unity element. If a ring contains an element u such that $ua = au = a$ for every a in the ring, u is called the unity element. We shall denote it either by u or the number 1. It can be proved that the unity element is unique. For, if u' is a second unity element, we have $u \cdot u' = u' \cdot u = u' = u$.

The usual laws of the minus sign can be proved for the elements in a ring. As an illustration let us prove $(-a)(-b) = ab$. Form the sum $(-a)(-b) + (-a)b + ab$. We shall show that this sum equals both ab and $(-a)(-b)$. Applying the right distributive law to the last two terms, we have $(-a)(-b) + (-a + a)b = (-a)(-b) + 0 \cdot b = (-a)(-b)$. On the other hand, grouping the first two terms, we have $(-a)(-b + b) + ab = (-a) \cdot 0 + ab = ab$.

Exercises

1. If the elements of the ring of residue classes modulo 10 are denoted by $0, 1, 2, \cdots, 9$, exhibit -2, -3, $-(3 \cdot 2)$, $3(-2)$ and $(-3)2$.

2. Prove that in a ring

a) $-(ab) = (-a)b = a(-b)$;
b) $a(b - c) = ab - ac$.

3. Check that the postulates for a ring are satisfied in the following definition of a number ring: A set of complex numbers forms a ring if the sum, difference, and product of any two numbers in the set are again in the set.

2 · Integral domains and fields

Rings may be specialized in many ways. We shall be interested particularly in the commutative rings that are integral domains or fields.

Integral domain. A commutative ring of at least two elements is an integral domain if it contains a unity element u and no proper divisors of zero.*

Field. An integral domain is a field if every element $a \neq 0$ has a multiplicative inverse a^{-1} such that $a^{-1} \cdot a = u$.

In the above examples we note that the integers form an integral domain but not a field, that the even integers form a ring but not an integral domain, and that the residue classes modulo m form a field if and only if m is a prime. The rational numbers, the real numbers, and the complex numbers are examples of fields with respect to the operations addition and multiplication. Note that the rational numbers and the real numbers are subfields of the field of complex numbers. We define a *subfield* to be a subset of elements of a field that itself forms a field with respect to the given operations.

Of interest is a second definition of a field which is easily proved to be equivalent to the first definition.

Second definition of a field. A set of at least two elements forms a field with respect to two operations addition and multiplication, if

    a) it is closed with respect to addition and multiplication;

    b) it forms a commutative group with respect to addition, whose identity is called the zero element;

    c) its nonzero elements form a commutative group with respect

---

* Some authors do not demand a unity element for an integral domain. See van der Waerden, *Moderne Algebra*, Vol. 1, p. 37, and Dubreil, *Algèbre*, Vol. 1, p. 112.

to multiplication, whose identity is called the unity element;
d) the distributive laws hold: $a(b + c) = ab + ac$ and $(b + c)a = ba + ca$.

Exercises

Determine whether the following sets with respect to addition and multiplication are rings. If they are rings, are they fields or integral domains?

1. The positive integers.
2. Numbers of the form $b\sqrt{2}$, with b rational.
3. Numbers of the form $3m$, with m an integer.
4. The fourth roots of unity.
5. 0.
6. Numbers of the form $a + b\sqrt{2}$, with a and b integers.
7. Numbers of the form $a + b\sqrt{2}$, with a and b rational.
8. Numbers of the form $a + bi$, with a and b integers.
9. Numbers of the form $a + bi$, with a and b rational.
10. The residue classes modulo 15.
11. The residue classes modulo 11.
12. The set of numbers $a + b\sqrt[3]{9}$, with a and b rational.
13. The set of numbers $a + b\sqrt[4]{2}$, with a and b rational.
14. The pairs of rational numbers (a, b) with equality, addition, and multiplication defined as follows: $(a, b) = (c, d)$ if and only if $a = c$ and $b = d$; $(a, b) + (c, d) = (a + c, b + d)$; $(a, b) \cdot (c, d) = (ac, bd)$.
15. In an integral domain prove that $ax = ay$, $a \neq 0$, implies $x = y$.
16. Prove: The equation $ax = b$, where $a \neq 0$, has a unique solution x in a field. Thus division except by zero is always possible in a field.
17. Check that the postulates for a field are satisfied in the following definition of a number field: A set of at least two complex numbers forms a field if the sum, difference, product, and quotient of any two numbers are again numbers of the set. Division by zero is excluded.

3 · Quotients in a field

In a field the unique solution $a^{-1}b$ of the equation $ax = b$, where $a \neq 0$, is often denoted by the quotient b/a. For example, in the residue class ring modulo 5, $2/3$ means $2 \cdot 3^{-1} = 2 \cdot 2 = 4$. We may prove that the following rules govern quotients:

1) $a/b = c/d$ if and only if $ad = bc$;
2) $a/b + c/d = (ad + bc)/(bd)$;
3) $(a/b)(c/d) = (ac)/(bd)$.

Since these rules can easily be proved from the definition of a quotient, their proof is left to the student.

Exercises

1. In the ring of residue classes modulo 7 exhibit $\frac{1}{3}$, $-\frac{1}{3}$, $-\frac{3}{5}$.
2. Prove that in a field

    a) $(a/b) - (c/d) = (ad - bc)/bd$;
    b) if $a/b \neq 0$, then $(a/b)(b/a) = u$;
    c) $(-a)^{-1} = -(a^{-1})$;
    d) $-(a/b) = (-a)/b = a/(-b)$;
    e) $(-a)/(-b) = a/b$.

4 · Quotient field

Just as the rational numbers were constructed from the integers so that the rational numbers contained a subset isomorphic to the integers, a field can be constructed from the elements of an integral domain such that a subset of the elements of the field is isomorphic to the integral domain. We say that the integral domain is embedded in the field.

Theorem 1. A field may be constructed from the elements of an integral domain.

The field that we shall construct is called the quotient field of the integral domain. Let $a, b, c, \cdots$ be the elements of the integral domain I. Consider the ordered pairs of elements (a, b), with $b \neq 0$. We define equality of two pairs as follows: $(a, b) = (c, d)$ if and only if $ad = bc$. This equality is an equivalence relation, for it is easily seen to be symmetric and reflexive, and it is easily proved to be transitive. If $(a, b) = (c, d)$ and if $(c, d) = (e, f)$, then $ad = bc$ and $cf = de$. Hence $adf = bcf = bde$. Since $d \neq 0$, we can apply the cancellation law for multiplication (see Exercise 15, p. 61) and obtain $af = be$, the required condition for the equality of (a, b) and (e, f). Thus we see that the pairs (a, b) are separated into classes of equal pairs. A given class can be represented by any pair in it.

Let (a, b) and (c, d) be representatives of any two classes. We define the sum and product of two classes represented by (a, b) and (c, d) as the classes whose representatives are obtained as follows:

$$(a, b) + (c, d) = (ad + bc, bd),$$
$$(a, b) \cdot (c, d) = (ac, bd).$$

The student can check that the same sum and product classes are obtained if (a, b) is replaced by a pair $(a', b') = (a, b)$ and (c, d) is replaced by a pair $(c', d') = (c, d)$.

It remains to be proved that these classes form a field with respect to addition and multiplication. The details of the proof are left to the student. He should check that the associative, commutative, and distributive laws hold; that the zero element is $(0, a)$, where 0 is the zero of the integral domain; that the additive inverse of (a, b) is $(-a, b)$; that the unity element is (u, u), where u is the unity element of the integral domain; and that the multiplicative inverse of (a, b), where $a \neq 0$, is (b, a).

Theorem 2. The quotient field of an integral domain contains a subset of elements isomorphic to the integral domain.

We set up the following one-to-one correspondence between the elements $a, b, c, \cdots$ of the integral domain and the classes (a, u), (b, u), (c, u), $\cdots$ of the quotient field. Thus, if

$$(a, u) \leftrightarrow a \quad \text{and} \quad (b, u) \leftrightarrow b,$$

then

$$(a, u) + (b, u) = (au + bu, u^2) = (a + b, u) \leftrightarrow a + b$$

and

$$(a, u) \cdot (b, u) = (ab, u^2) = (ab, u) \leftrightarrow ab,$$

and the isomorphism is established.

If the integral domain I is already a subset of a field F, then the quotient field of I is isomorphic to a subfield of the field F. For we may set up the one-to-one correspondence $(a, b) \leftrightarrow a/b = ab^{-1}$, where a and $b \neq 0$ are elements of the integral domain. Note that in general b^{-1} is not an element of the integral domain. Hence it is seen why the quotient field was given its name. Moreover, it can be proved that the quotient field is a minimum extension of the integral domain I to a field in the sense that any field containing I contains a subfield isomorphic to the quotient field of the integral domain.

Examples. Let F be the field of real numbers and I the integral domain of integers. The quotient field of I is then the field of rational numbers, a subfield of F.

Determine the quotient field of the integral domain of residue classes modulo 3.   Here the classes of the quotient field are

$$0: \quad (0,1),\ (0,2);$$
$$1: \quad (1,1),\ (2,2);$$
$$2: \quad (2,1),\ (1,2).$$

We see that the quotient field is isomorphic to the integral domain of residue classes modulo 3 itself.

Exercises

1. Prove that the sum and product classes of the quotient field are independent of the particular pairs (a, b) and (c, d) used in the definition.

2. Prove that the classes of the quotient field of an integral domain obey the associative and commutative laws for addition and multiplication, and the distributive law.

3. Prove that the multiplicative inverse of the class represented by (a, b), where $a \neq 0$, is the class represented by (b, a).

4. What is the quotient field of the integral domain of residue classes modulo 5?

5. What is the quotient field of the integral domain of complex numbers $a + bi$, where a and b are integers?

5 · Polynomials over an integral domain

Let x be an arbitrary symbol which is commutative with the elements of an integral domain I.   For n a positive integer let $x^n = x \cdot x \cdots x$ to n factors.   Further, we define $u \cdot x = x$, where u is the unity element of I.   A polynomial over the integral domain I is a finite expression of the form

$$(1) \qquad f(x) = a_0 + a_1 x + a_2 x^2 + \cdots + a_n x^n,$$

where the coefficients a_i are elements of I.   The power of x multiplying a_0 is x^0, which is defined to equal u.   If a power of x does not appear in $f(x)$, its coefficient is considered to be zero.

Two polynomials are equal if and only if the coefficients of like powers of x are equal; i.e., if and only if they are identical.   In this definition of equality the polynomials are regarded as forms; we are not discussing their functional values.   Keep in mind that x is an arbitrary symbol to which we at present are assigning no value.   It is called an *indeterminate*.

We now define the sum and product of two polynomials.   Let $f(x)$ be the polynomial (1), and let $g(x)$ be the polynomial

$$(2) \qquad g(x) = b_0 + b_1 x + b_2 x^2 + \cdots + b_m x^m,$$

the b_i being elements in I.   Then

(3) $f(x) \pm g(x) = (a_0 \pm b_0) + (a_1 \pm b_1)x + \cdots$
$$+ (a_m \pm b_m)x^m + a_{m+1}x^{m+1} + \cdots + a_n x^n, \qquad m < n,$$
and

(4) $f(x) \cdot g(x) = a_0 b_0 + (a_0 b_1 + a_1 b_0)x$
$$+ (a_0 b_2 + a_1 b_1 + a_2 b_0)x^2 + \cdots + a_n b_m x^{n+m},$$

the coefficient of x^k being

$$a_0 b_k + a_1 b_{k-1} + a_2 b_{k-2} + \cdots + a_k b_0.$$

If $a_n \neq 0$, then n is called the *degree* of the polynomial $f(x)$. Note that the polynomials of zero degree are the nonzero elements of the integral domain I. The polynomial zero has no degree. Also note that the degree of the product of two polynomials is the sum $m + n$ of the degrees of the factors.

Theorem 3.   The polynomials (1) over an integral domain I with sum and product defined by (3) and (4) form an integral domain.

This integral domain is denoted by $I[x]$. The proof in detail is left to the student. The commutative, associative, and distributive laws can be verified. The zero element and the unity element are obviously the zero element and the unity element of the integral domain of coefficients. There are no proper zero divisors, for if $f(x)$ and $g(x)$ are given by (1) and (2) with $a_n \neq 0$ and $b_m \neq 0$, the product (4) is not zero, since $a_n b_m = 0$ if and only if $a_n = 0$ or if $b_m = 0$.

6 · Characteristic of an integral domain

Let u be the unity element of the integral domain I. The unity element generates an additive cyclic group. If k is a positive integer, $ku = u + u + \cdots + u$ with k terms. Interpreting additively the definitions and exponent laws derived for the powers of an element of a group, we have $0 \cdot u = 0$, $(-k)u = k(-u)$, $ru + su = (r + s)u$, and $s(ru) = (sr)u = r(su)$. Now, as we have seen, a cyclic group is isomorphic either to the additive group of integers or to the additive group of residue classes modulo m. In the latter case we shall prove that m is a prime.

Theorem 4. If the additive cyclic group generated by u, *the unity element of an integral domain, is of order* m > 0, m *is a prime* p.

Let $m = rs$. Then $(ru)(su) = (u+u+\cdots+u)(u+u+\cdots+u) =$
$\underbrace{}_{r\text{ terms}}\ \underbrace{}_{s\text{ terms}}$
$\underbrace{u^2 + u^2 + \cdots + u^2}_{rs\text{ terms}} = (rs)u^2 = (rs)u = 0$. But ru and su are elements of the integral domain, which has no proper zero divisors. Hence $ru = 0$ or $su = 0$, contradicting the order m of the cyclic group generated by u. Thus m is a prime p.

Definition. The order of the additive cyclic group generated by the unity element u of an integral domain is called the characteristic of the integral domain. Thus the characteristic is either a positive prime p or zero.

Theorem 5. An integral domain whose characteristic is zero contains a subset of elements which is isomorphic to the integral domain of integers, and an integral domain whose characteristic is a prime p *contains a subset of elements which is isomorphic to the field of residue classes modulo* p.

If the cyclic group generated by u is of order zero, then the elements ku are distinct and the one-to-one correspondence $ku \leftrightarrow k$ is an isomorphism, for, if $ru \leftrightarrow r$ and $su \leftrightarrow s$, then $ru + su = (r + s)u \leftrightarrow r + s$, and $(ru)(su) = (rs)u \leftrightarrow rs$. If the cyclic group generated by u is of prime order p, the elements ku for which k belongs to the same residue class modulo p are equal, and the correspondence $ku \leftrightarrow C_k$, where C_k denotes the residue class containing the integer k, gives us an isomorphism between the elements ku and the residue classes modulo p.

Theorem 6. In an integral domain all nonzero elements generate additive cyclic groups of the same order.

Let u be the unity element, and let a be any nonzero element of the integral domain. For an integral domain of characteristic p, it is easily checked that $pa = p(au) = p(ua) = (pu)a = 0$. Moreover, if $ma = 0$, where $a \neq 0$ and $m \neq 0$, then $ma = m(ua) = (mu)a = 0$, and hence $mu = 0$, giving us $m = kp$. For an integral domain of characteristic zero, $ma \neq 0$ if $a \neq 0$ and $m \neq 0$, for again $ma = (mu)a$ and $mu \neq 0$, for $m \neq 0$.

Since fields are integral domains, they may also be separated into two essentially different types, fields of characteristic a prime

p and fields of characteristic zero. The quotient field of the integral domain of integral multiples of the unity element u is, in the case of characteristic p, isomorphic to the field of residue classes modulo p, and in the case of characteristic zero isomorphic to the field of rational numbers. Thus a field contains a subfield that is isomorphic either to the field of residue classes modulo p or to the field of rational numbers.

7 · Division in an integral domain

We shall now list some definitions that are used in any integral domain, and we shall see that they are similar to the corresponding definitions given when the divisibility properties of integers were studied.

Divisor. An element b in an integral domain I is a divisor of an element a in I, if there exists in I an element c such that $a = bc$.

Associates and units. Two nonzero elements a and b in an integral domain I are associates if a divides b and b divides a. A unit is an associate of the unity element of I.

Theorem 7. An element a *in an integral domain* I *is a unit in* I *if and only if it has a multiplicative inverse in* I.

Now, if a is a unit, it divides u the unity element of I, and we have $ab = u$. Thus b is a multiplicative inverse of a. On the other hand, if a has a multiplicative inverse b, $ab = u$ and a divides u. The unity element u divides any element a in I, for $au = a$. Hence a is a unit. Thus those and only those elements in I are units which have multiplicative inverses in I.

Theorem 8. Two elements in I *are associates if and only if one is a unit times the other.*

Let a and b be associates in I. Then $a = bc$ and $b = ad$. Thus $a = adc$, but $a = au$, and hence $au = adc$. Applying the cancellation law for multiplication, we have $u = dc$, which says that c and d are units. Thus, if two elements are associates, one is a unit times the other. On the other hand, if $b = au'$, where u' is a unit such that $u'u'' = u$, then b divides a, for $a = au = a(u'u'') = (au')u'' = bu''$. Note that we have also proved that any element a is divisible by the units of the integral domain.

Proper and improper divisors. Any nonzero element a in an integral domain is divisible by its associates and the units of the integral domain.   These divisors of a are called improper divisors of a.   All other divisors are called proper divisors.

Prime or irreducible element.   A nonzero element a of an integral domain which is not a unit and which has no proper divisors is a prime or irreducible element.   If an element has proper divisors, it is called reducible.

Examples.   Since in a field every nonzero element has a multiplicative inverse, the units of a field are its nonzero elements.

In the polynomial domain $I[x]$ the units are the units of the integral domain I of coefficients.   To prove this fact let $f(x) \cdot g(x) = u$, the unity element of I.   Since the degree of the product of two polynomials is the sum of the degrees of the factors, both $f(x)$ and $g(x)$ must be polynomials of degree zero.

In the polynomial domain $F[x]$, where F is a field, the associates of the polynomial $f(x)$ are $cf(x)$, where c is any nonzero element of the field.

In the integral domain of integers the prime integers are the irreducible elements.

The polynomial $x^2 - 2$ is irreducible over the field of rational numbers, but since $(x - \sqrt{2})(x + \sqrt{2}) = x^2 - 2$, the polynomial $x^2 - 2$ is reducible over the field of real numbers.   Note that irreducibility is thus a property dependent upon the particular integral domain considered.

To illustrate somewhat further the above definitions, consider the integral domain whose elements are of the form $a + b\sqrt{13}$, where a and b are integers.   It is left to the student to fill in the proofs that are omitted in the following examples.   Let $\alpha = a + b\sqrt{13}$.   We define $N(\alpha) = (a + b\sqrt{13})(a - b\sqrt{13}) = a^2 - 13b^2$, which we note is an integer. $N(\alpha)$ is called the norm of α.

1. Prove that $N(\alpha\beta) = N(\alpha)N(\beta)$.

2. The element α is a unit if and only if $N(\alpha) = \pm 1$.

If $N(\alpha) = \pm 1$, then α is a unit, for $(a + b\sqrt{13})(a - b\sqrt{13}) = \pm 1$, and $a + b\sqrt{13}$ divides the unity element 1.   If α is a unit, we have $\alpha\beta = 1$, and hence $N(\alpha\beta) = N(\alpha)N(\beta) = 1$.   As $N(\alpha)$ and $N(\beta)$ are integers, $N(\alpha) = \pm 1$ and $N(\beta) = \pm 1$.

3. $18 - 5\sqrt{13}$ and $-18 - 5\sqrt{13}$ are units.

4. $1 + \sqrt{13}$ and $-47 + 13\sqrt{13}$ are associates, but not units.

5. 2, $-3 - \sqrt{13}$, and $3 - \sqrt{13}$ are primes. Let $\alpha\beta = 2$. Then $N(\alpha\beta) = N(\alpha)N(\beta) = 4$. Thus the prime 2 divides $N(\alpha)$ or $N(\beta)$. Let $N(\alpha) = \pm 2$ or ± 4. If $N(\alpha) = \pm 4$, $N(\beta) = \pm 1$ and β is a unit. Hence α is an improper divisor. Let $N(\alpha) = \pm 2$. Then $a^2 - 13b^2 = \pm 2$, and $a^2 \equiv \pm 2 \pmod{13}$. It is easily seen by substitution that this congruence has no solutions. Hence 2 is a prime or irreducible element in the integral domain $a + b\sqrt{13}$.

6. Note that $4 = 2 \cdot 2 = (-3 - \sqrt{13})(3 - \sqrt{13})$, and hence the unique factorization into prime or irreducible elements does not hold.

Exercises

1. In the integral domain $F[x]$, where F is the field of rational numbers, is the polynomial $2x^2 - 2$ a divisor of $x^2 - 1$; is $2x^2 - 2$ divisible by the polynomial 3? Show the factorization if the answer is yes.

2. What are the units of the integral domain of residue classes modulo 5?

3. What are the units of the integral domain of complex numbers of the form $a + bi$, where a and b are rational?

4. Are 1, -1, i, $-i$ units in the integral domain of complex numbers of the form $a + bi$, where a and b are integers?

The divisibility concepts discussed in this section will be applied in the next chapter to the particular integral domain of polynomials over a field.

5

Polynomials over a Field

---

1 · Division algorithm

We now establish divisibility properties of polynomials over a field which are analogous to the divisibility properties of the integers.

Theorem 1.   Division algorithm.   If $g(x) \neq 0$ *and* $f(x)$ *are any two polynomials over a field* F, *there exist unique polynomials* $q(x)$ *and* $r(x)$ *over* F *such that*

$$f(x) = g(x) \cdot q(x) + r(x),$$

where $r(x)$ *either is zero or of degree less than the degree of* $g(x)$.

Let

$$f(x) = a_0 + a_1 x + \cdots + a_n x^n \qquad a_n \neq 0$$

and

$$g(x) = b_0 + b_1 x + \cdots + b_m x^m, \qquad b_m \neq 0.$$

If $f(x)$ is zero or if the degree of $f(x)$ is less than the degree m of $g(x)$, we have the representation

$$f(x) = 0 \cdot g(x) + f(x).$$

Thus let $n \geq m$.   Then form the difference

$$(1) \qquad f(x) - \frac{a_n}{b_m} x^{n-m} g(x) = f_1(x).$$

Now $f_1(x)$ is a polynomial over F of degree less than n.   We make the proof by induction.   Assume the algorithm true for all polynomials over F of degree less than n.   Since $f_1(x)$ is such a polynomial, we may write

$$(2) \qquad f_1(x) = q_1(x) \cdot g(x) + r(x),$$

70

where $r(x)$ is either zero or of degree less than the degree of $g(x)$. We may then write (1) with the aid of (2) as

$$f(x) - \frac{a_n}{b_m} x^{n-m} g(x) = q_1(x) \cdot g(x) + r(x),$$

and hence

$$f(x) = \left[\frac{a_n}{b_m} x^{n-m} + q_1(x)\right] \cdot g(x) + r(x)$$

$$= q(x) \cdot g(x) + r(x),$$

and we have the desired representation of $f(x)$.

It remains to be proved that the polynomials $q(x)$ and $r(x)$ are unique. Suppose that there is a second pair of polynomials $q'(x)$ and $r'(x)$ such that

$$f(x) = q'(x) \cdot g(x) + r'(x),$$

where $r'(x)$ is either zero or of degree less than the degree of $g(x)$. Hence

$$q'(x) \cdot g(x) + r'(x) = q(x) \cdot g(x) + r(x)$$

and

$$g(x)[q'(x) - q(x)] = r(x) - r'(x).$$

Now the right-hand side of this equation is either zero or of degree less than the degree of $g(x)$. Thus, unless $q'(x) - q(x) = 0$, we have a contradiction. Consequently, $q'(x) = q(x)$ and $r(x) = r'(x)$.

The polynomial $q(x)$ is called the *quotient*, and the polynomial $r(x)$ is called the *remainder* in the division algorithm.

Corollary 1. Remainder theorem. The remainder when a polynomial $f(x)$ *is divided by* $x - a$ *is* $f(a)$.

This is immediate from the division algorithm, for when we replace $g(x)$ by $x - a$ the remainder becomes r, an element in the field, and we have $f(a) = (a - a) \cdot q(a) + r = r$. Thus $f(x) = (x - a) \cdot q(x) + f(a)$. From this last formula we see immediately that $f(x)$ has the factor $x - a$ if and only if $f(a) = 0$. Hence we have the following corollary known as the factor theorem.

Corollary 2. A polynomial $f(x)$ *is divisible by* $x - a$ *if and only if* $f(a) = 0$.

Definition. An element a is called a zero of a polynomial $f(x)$ if $f(a) = 0$.

2 · Synthetic division

To facilitate finding the quotient $q(x)$ and the remainder r when a polynomial $f(x)$ over a field F is divided by the polynomial $x - c$ over F, we introduce the method of synthetic division or detached coefficients.   Let

$$f(x) = a_0 + a_1 x + \cdots + a_{n-1} x^{n-1} + a_n x^n$$

and

$$q(x) = b_0 + b_1 x + \cdots + b_{n-1} x^{n-1}.$$

Then

$$\begin{aligned} f(x) &= (x - c)q(x) + r \\ &= (r - cb_0) + (b_0 - cb_1)x + (b_1 - cb_2)x^2 + \cdots \\ &\quad + (b_{n-2} - cb_{n-1})x^{n-1} + b_{n-1}x^n. \end{aligned}$$

Equating coefficients of $f(x)$ when we express it in these two ways, we have

$$a_n = b_{n-1}, a_{n-1} = b_{n-2} - cb_{n-1}, \cdots, a_1 = b_0 - cb_1, a_0 = r - cb_0.$$

For computation purposes the work may be arranged as follows:

a_n	a_{n-1}	$\cdots$	a_1	a_0	$\lfloor c$
	cb_{n-1}	$\cdots$	cb_1	cb_0	
$b_{n-1} = a_n$	$b_{n-2} = a_{n-1} + cb_{n-1}$	$\cdots$	$b_0 = a_1 + cb_1$	$r = a_0 + cb_0.$	

Thus by merely listing the coefficients and performing a simple multiplication and addition, we can read off the quotient and the remainder from the last line.

Example. Find the quotient and the remainder when the polynomial $3x^3 - 4x + 2$ is divided by $x + 3$. Using synthetic division, we have

$$\begin{array}{rrrr|r} 3 & 0 & -4 & 2 & \underline{-3} \\ & -9 & 27 & -69 & \\ \hline 3 & -9 & 23 & -67, & \end{array}$$

which gives $3x^2 - 9x + 23$ as the quotient and -67 as the remainder.

Exercises

1. Find the quotient and the remainder when

a) $-x^4 + 7x^3 + 10x^2 - 5$ is divided by $x - 2$;
b) $3x^5 + 6x^3 - 3x$ is divided by $x + 1$;
c) $x^3 + i$ is divided by $x - i$.

2. If $f(x) = 2x^3 + 3x^2 - 1$, find $f(2), f(-3), f(i)$.

3. In the field of residue classes modulo 5, exhibit the quotient and the remainder when the polynomial $3x^3 - 4x^2 + 2x - 2$ is divided by $2x^2 + 1$.

4. Are the following polynomials reducible or irreducible over the field of residue classes modulo 5? over the field of residue classes modulo 7?

a) $x^2 - x + 3$. *mod 5 only*
b) $x^3 + 3x^2 + x - 4$. *mod 9 only*

3 · Greatest common divisor

Monic polynomial. A polynomial is called monic if the coefficient of the highest power of x is the unity element of the field.

Greatest common divisor. A polynomial $d(x)$ is a greatest common divisor of two polynomials $f(x)$ and $g(x)$ if $d(x)$ divides $f(x)$ and $g(x)$, and, if $a(x)$ is a common divisor of $f(x)$ and $g(x)$, then $a(x)$ divides $d(x)$. We note that, if a greatest common divisor $d(x) \neq 0$ exists, then any associate of $d(x)$ is also a greatest common divisor of $f(x)$ and $g(x)$. We often speak of that associate of $d(x)$ which is monic as *the* greatest common divisor of $f(x)$ and $g(x)$.

Theorem 2. Euclidean algorithm. Two nonzero polynomials $f(x)$ *and* $g(x)$ *over a field* F *have a greatest common divisor* $d(x)$ *over* F.

The proof is the same as the proof for the construction of the greatest common divisor of two nonzero integers. We apply the division algorithm to $f(x)$ and $g(x)$, obtaining

$$(3) \qquad f(x) = g(x) \cdot q(x) + r(x),$$

where $r(x)$ is either zero or of degree less than the degree of $g(x)$. If $r(x)$ is zero, then a greatest common divisor of $f(x)$ and $g(x)$ is $g(x)$ itself. If $r(x) \neq 0$, we prove that a greatest common divisor of $f(x)$ and $g(x)$ is a greatest common divisor of $g(x)$ and $r(x)$, thus reducing the problem of finding a g.c.d. of $f(x)$ and $g(x)$ to that of finding a g.c.d. of $g(x)$ and $r(x)$. Let $d(x)$ be a greatest common divisor of $f(x)$ and $g(x)$, and let $d'(x)$ be a greatest common divisor of $g(x)$ and $r(x)$. Since $d'(x)$ divides $g(x)$ and $r(x)$, we see by (3) that it divides $f(x)$, and hence it is a common divisor of $f(x)$ and $g(x)$. Therefore $d'(x)$ divides $d(x)$. Similarly (3) shows that $d(x)$ divides $r(x)$, and thus $d'(x)$ is divisible by $d(x)$. Hence $d(x)$ and $d'(x)$ are associates and differ only by a factor that is an element of F.

Now apply the division algorithm to $g(x)$ and $r(x)$, obtaining

$$g(x) = r(x) \cdot q_1(x) + r_1(x),$$

where $r_1(x)$ is either zero or of degree less than the degree of $r(x)$. If $r_1(x) = 0$, then $r(x)$ is a greatest common divisor of $f(x)$ and $g(x)$. If $r_1(x) \neq 0$, then we have, as before, that a g.c.d. of $g(x)$ and $r(x)$ is a g.c.d. of $r(x)$ and $r_1(x)$, thus reducing the problem of finding a g.c.d. of $f(x)$ and $g(x)$ to the problem of finding a g.c.d. of $r(x)$ and $r_1(x)$. We can continue in this manner, obtaining the sequence of equations

$$f(x) = g(x) \cdot q(x) + r(x),$$

$$g(x) = r(x) \cdot q_1(x) + r_1(x),$$

$$r(x) = r_1(x) \cdot q_2(x) + r_2(x),$$

$$\cdot$$
$$\cdot$$
$$\cdot$$

$$(4) \qquad r_j(x) = r_{j+1}(x) \cdot q_{j+2}(x) + r_{j+2}(x),$$

$$\cdot$$
$$\cdot$$
$$\cdot$$

$$r_{n-2}(x) = r_{n-1}(x) \cdot q_n(x) + r_n(x),$$

$$r_{n-1}(x) = r_n(x) \cdot q_{n+1}(x).$$

The process shows that we must finally obtain a zero remainder, for a given remainder $r_j(x)$ is either zero or of degree less than the degree of the preceding remainder $r_{j-1}(x)$. We note that a polynomial of degree zero, i.e., an element of the field, divides every polynomial over the field. Hence, if the process does not end before we obtain a polynomial of degree zero, the next step assures us of a zero remainder. The last nonzero remainder $r_n(x)$ is a g.c.d. of $f(x)$ and $g(x)$, for, denoting a g.c.d. of $f(x)$ and $g(x)$ by (f, g), we have $(f, g) = (g, r) = (r, r_1) = \cdots = (r_{n-2}, r_{n-1}) = (r_{n-1}, r_n) = r_n$.

In the actual computation of a g.c.d. of two polynomials the work may be simplified by multiplying one or more of the remainders or the given polynomials by a nonzero element of the field. Since all g.c.d.'s are associates, this multiplication does not change *the* g.c.d. The last remainder is merely multiplied by an element of the field. Further, it should be noted that the process of finding a g.c.d. involves only rational operations on the coefficients of the given polynomials. Thus the coefficients of a g.c.d. are always elements in the least field containing the coefficients of the given polynomial.

Theorem 3. Let $d(x)$ *be a g.c.d. of the two polynomials* $f(x)$ *and* $g(x)$ *over the field* F. *Then there exist polynomials* $m(x)$ *and* $n(x)$ *over* F *such that*

$$d(x) = m(x) \cdot g(x) + n(x) \cdot f(x).$$

This can be proved by expressing the successive remainders in equations (4) in terms of $f(x)$ and $g(x)$, thus:

$$r(x) = f(x) - g(x) \cdot q(x),$$

$$r_1(x) = g(x) - r(x) \cdot q_1(x) = g(x) - q_1(x)[f(x) - g(x) \cdot q(x)]$$

$$= -q_1(x) \cdot f(x) + [1 + q(x) \cdot q_1(x)]g(x), \text{ etc.}$$

A general proof can be given by induction. Let

$$r_j(x) = m_j(x) \cdot g(x) + n_j(x) \cdot f(x)$$

for all $j < k$. Denoting $r(x)$ by $r_0(x)$, we see that $r_j(x)$ has been expressed in the desired form for $j = 0, 1$. From equations (4) we have

$$r_{k-2}(x) = r_{k-1}(x) \cdot q_k(x) + r_k(x).$$

Solving this equation for $r_k(x)$ and substituting the values for $r_{k-1}(x)$ and $r_{k-2}(x)$ as given by our induction hypothesis, we have

$$r_k(x) = -q_k(x)[m_{k-1}(x) \cdot g(x) + n_{k-1}(x) \cdot f(x)]$$
$$+ [m_{k-2}(x) \cdot g(x) + n_{k-2}(x) \cdot f(x)]$$
$$= [-q_k(x) \cdot m_{k-1}(x) + m_{k-2}(x)]g(x) + [-q_k(x) \cdot n_{k-1}(x)$$
$$+ n_{k-2}(x)]f(x),$$

and the induction is complete.

Definition. Two polynomials $f(x)$ and $g(x)$ over a field F are said to be relatively prime if their greatest common divisor is the unity element of F.

Example. Find the g.c.d. of the two polynomials $f(x) = x^5 + 2x^3 + x^2 + 2x + 3$ and $g(x) = x^4 + x^3 + 4x^2 + 3x + 3$ over the field of residue classes modulo 5 and express it in the form $m(x) \cdot g(x) + n(x) \cdot f(x)$. We find

$$f(x) = g(x)(x + 4) + 4x^3 + 2x^2 + 2x + 1,$$

$$g(x) = (4x^3 + 2x^2 + 2x + 1)(4x + 2) + 2x^2 + 1,$$

$$4x^3 + 2x^2 + 2x + 1 = (2x^2 + 1)(2x + 1).$$

Therefore $2x^2 + 1$ is a g.c.d., and its monic associate $x^2 + 3$ is the g.c.d. To express the g.c.d. in the desired form, we use the above equations, obtaining

$$2x^2 + 1 = g(x) - (4x^3 + 2x^2 + 2x + 1)(4x + 2)$$

$$= g(x) - [f(x) - g(x)(x + 4)](4x + 2)$$

$$= (4x^2 + 3x + 4)g(x) - (4x + 2)f(x),$$

and

$$x^2 + 3 = (2x^2 + 4x + 2)g(x) + (3x + 4)f(x).$$

Exercises

1. Find the greatest common divisor of the two polynomials $f(x)$ and $g(x)$ over the indicated field of coefficients and express it in the form $m(x) \cdot g(x) + n(x) \cdot f(x)$.

a) $f(x) = x^5 - x^4 - 6x^3 - 2x^2 + 5x + 3,$ $g(x) = x^3 - 3x - 2.$
b) $f(x) = x^4 - 5x^3 + 6x^2 + 4x - 8,$ $g(x) = x^3 - x^2 - 4x + 4.$
c) $f(x) = x^4 - 4ix + 3,$ $g(x) = x^3 - i.$

2. Find the g.c.d. of the following pairs of polynomials:

a) $f(x) = 4x^4 - 4x^3 + 5x^2 - 4x + 1,$ $g(x) = 8x^3 - 6x^2 + 5x - 2.$
b) $f(x) = x^4 + x^3 + 2x^2 + x + 1,$ $g(x) = x^3 - 1.$

3. Find the g.c.d. of the following pairs of polynomials over the field of residue classes modulo 3:

a) $f(x) = x^5 + 2x^3 + x^2 + 2x,$ $g(x) = x^4 + x^3 + x^2.$
b) $f(x) = x^3 + 2x^2 + 2x + 1,$ $g(x) = x^2 + 2.$

4. Determine the constant c if the greatest common divisor of $f(x)$ and

$g(x)$ is linear. For each value of c obtained, what is the greatest common divisor?

a) $f(x) = x^3 + cx^2 - x + 2c$, $\qquad g(x) = x^2 + cx - 2$. $\qquad c = \sqrt{-1}$

b) $f(x) = x^2 + (c - 6)x + 2c - 1$, $\qquad g(x) = x^2 + (c + 2)x + 2c$.

4 · Factorization theorems

We continue with our list of theorems for polynomials over a field which are analogous to the theorems proved for integers.

Theorem 4. If $p(x)$ *is an irreducible polynomial over a field* F *and if* $p(x)$ *divides the product* $f(x) \cdot g(x)$ *of two polynomials over* F, *then* $p(x)$ *divides* $f(x)$ *or* $p(x)$ *divides* $g(x)$.

Suppose that $p(x)$ does not divide $f(x)$. Since $p(x)$ is irreducible over F, its only divisors are its associates and the units of the field. Hence $p(x)$ and $f(x)$ are relatively prime and their g.c.d. is the unity element u of the field. Thus there exist polynomials $m(x)$ and $n(x)$ over F such that

$$u = m(x) \cdot p(x) + n(x) \cdot f(x).$$

Multiply this equation by $g(x)$

$$g(x) = m(x) \cdot p(x) \cdot g(x) + n(x) \cdot f(x) \cdot g(x).$$

Using the hypothesis that $p(x)$ divides $f(x) \cdot g(x)$, we see that $p(x)$ is a factor of the left-hand side of the equation, and the theorem is established.

The proofs of the next two theorems are left to the student.

Theorem 5. If an irreducible polynomial $p(x)$ *over a field* F *divides the product of* n *polynomials* $q_1(x) \cdot q_2(x) \cdots q_n(x)$ *over* F, *it divides some factor* $q_i(x)$.

Theorem 6. If $f(x)$ *and* $g(x)$ *are relatively prime polynomials over a field* F, *and if* $f(x)$ *divides the product* $g(x) \cdot h(x)$ *over* F, *then* $f(x)$ *divides* $h(x)$.

Theorem 7. Unique factorization theorem. A polynomial $f(x)$ *of positive degree over a field* F *can be expressed as an element of* F *times a product of monic irreducible polynomials over* F. *This decomposition is unique except for the order in which the factors occur.*

We first prove that such a decomposition is possible. If $f(x)$ is irreducible, the decomposition is accomplished. Note that if

$f(x)$ is of degree 1 it is irreducible. Then let $f(x) = g(x) \cdot h(x)$. Now $g(x)$ and $h(x)$ are polynomials of degree less than the degree of $f(x)$. Hence we can make the induction hypothesis that the decomposition is possible for all polynomials of degree less than the degree of $f(x)$. Thus

$$g(x) = c \, p_1(x) \cdot p_2(x) \cdots p_r(x)$$

and

$$h(x) = c' \, p_1'(x) \cdot p_2'(x) \cdots p_s'(x),$$

where c and c' are elements of the field, and where $p_i(x)$ and $p_i'(x)$ are monic irreducible polynomials over F. We have then

$$f(x) = g(x) \cdot h(x) = cc' \, p_1(x) \cdots p_r(x) \cdot p_1'(x) \cdots p_s'(x).$$

Thus the induction is completed and the decomposition is accomplished.

It remains to be proved that the decomposition is unique. Assume the existence of two decompositions

$$f(x) = c \, p_1(x) \cdot p_2(x) \cdots p_n(x)$$
$$= d \, q_1(x) \cdot q_2(x) \cdots q_m(x).$$

Since these irreducible polynomials are monic, $c = d$. Since $p_1(x)$ is irreducible, it divides some $q_i(x)$. As both $p_1(x)$ and $q_i(x)$ are monic and irreducible, their quotient is the unity element of the field, and hence $p_1(x) = q_i(x)$. Dividing by this common factor and c, we obtain

$$f_1(x) = p_2(x) \cdots p_n(x) = q_1(x) \cdots q_{i-1}(x) \cdot q_{i+1}(x) \cdots q_m(x).$$

Now $f_1(x)$ is a polynomial of degree less than the degree of $f(x)$. Consequently, we can make an induction hypothesis to the effect that the decomposition is unique for all polynomials of degree less than the degree of $f(x)$. Thus the decomposition of $f_1(x)$ is unique, $n = m$, and the two sets of polynomials are identical. Hence we have the unique decomposition of $f(x)$.

Exercises

1. Prove the two theorems on p. 77 whose proofs were left to the student.

2. List the monic polynomials of the second degree over the field of residue classes modulo 3. Which are irreducible? Find the decomposition of the reducible polynomials. $x^2 + 2 = (x+1)(x+2)$

3. Find the decomposition of the following polynomials over the field of

$\textcircled{9}$ $d(2)$ $poly$.

rational numbers and over the field of complex numbers: a) $x^3 - 1$, b) $x^4 - 1$, c) $x^6 - 1$. (Hint: Recall that the zeros of these polynomials are roots of unity.)

4. Find the decomposition of the following polynomials over the field of residue classes modulo 3: a) $x^4 + x + 2$, b) $2x^3 + x^2 + 1$.

5 · Zeros of a polynomial

Theorem 8. A polynomial f(x) *of positive degree* n *over a field* **F** *has at most* n *zeros in* **F**.

Let $f(x) = a_0 + a_1 x + \cdots + a_n x^n$, with $a_n \neq 0$. If $f(x)$ has a zero r_1, the factor theorem gives us $f(x) = (x - r_1)q(x)$. It is seen by substitution that a zero of $q(x)$ is a zero of $f(x)$. Thus $f(x)$ has r_1 and the zeros of $q(x)$ as zeros. On the other hand, $f(x)$ has no zeros other than r_1 and the zeros of $q(x)$, for, if a were a zero that is neither r_1 nor a zero of $q(x)$, we would have $f(a) = 0 = (a - r_1)q(a)$. Since neither $q(a)$ nor $a - r_1$ is zero and since there are no proper divisors of zero in a field, this equation is impossible. The proof can now be made by induction. The polynomial $q(x)$ is of degree $n - 1$, and hence we make the induction hypothesis that $q(x)$ has at most $n - 1$ zeros. Thus $f(x)$ has at most n zeros, and the proof is completed.

Theorem 9. If the polynomial f(x) $= a_0 + a_1 x + \cdots + a_n x^n$ *over a field* **F** *has the* n *zeros* r_1, r_2, $\cdots$, r_n *in* **F**, *then* f(x) *can be written uniquely as* $a_n(x - r_1)(x - r_2) \cdots (x - r_n)$.

Since r_1 is a zero, $f(x) = (x - r_1)q(x)$. As in the previous theorem, the zeros of $f(x)$ are r_1 and the zeros of $q(x)$. Hence the zeros of $q(x)$ are r_2, r_3, $\cdots$, r_n. Now we make the induction hypothesis that if a polynomial of degree $m < n$ has m zeros it can be written in factored form. Note that $q(x)$ is of degree $n - 1$ and that the coefficient of its highest power of x is a_n. Thus $q(x) = a_n(x - r_2)(x - r_3) \cdots (x - r_n)$, and $f(x) = (x - r_1)q(x)$ has the required factored form. The unique factorization theorem tells us that this decomposition is unique, for the $x - r_i$ are monic irreducible polynomials over **F**.

We give without proof the so-called fundamental theorem of algebra.

Theorem 10. A polynomial of positive degree over the field of complex numbers has a zero that is a complex number.

Theorem 11. A polynomial $f(x) = a_0 + a_1x + \cdots + a_nx^n$, *with* $a_n \neq 0$, *over the field of complex numbers has exactly* n *zeros that are complex numbers.*

By the fundamental theorem of algebra, $f(x)$ has a zero r_1 that is a complex number. Hence $f(x) = (x - r_1)q(x)$. Moreover, $q(x)$ is of degree $n - 1$, and, if $n - 1 > 0$, $q(x)$ has a root r_2 that is a complex number. We make the induction hypothesis that a polynomial of degree $m < n$ over the field of complex numbers has exactly m zeros. Hence $q(x)$ has exactly $n - 1$ zeros, and $f(x)$ has exactly n zeros, as was to be proved.

Hence by Theorem 9, $f(x)$ can be written uniquely in the form $f(x) = a_n(x - r_1)(x - r_2) \cdots (x - r_n)$. Thus the only irreducible monic polynomials over the field of complex numbers are linear.

We now specialize our field of coefficients to the field of real numbers and see what decomposition is given by the unique factorization theorem.

Theorem 12. If a polynomial $f(x)$ *over the field of real numbers has the zero* a + bi, *where* b $\neq$ 0, *it has the conjugate zero* a − bi.

Form the product $[x - (a + bi)][x - (a - bi)] = (x - a)^2 + b^2$, which we observe is a polynomial with real coefficients. Hence when we divide $f(x)$ by this polynomial we obtain a quotient and a remainder over the field of real numbers. Thus $f(x) = [(x - a)^2 + b^2]q(x) + r(x)$, where $r(x)$ is either zero or of degree 1 at most. We, of course, wish to prove that $r(x) = 0$. Let $r(x) = mx + n$. Now $f(a + bi) = 0 = m(a + bi) + n$. Therefore, $ma + n = 0$ and $mb = 0$. Since $b \neq 0$, $m = 0$, and hence $n = 0$. Thus $r(x) = 0$, and $f(x)$ has the factor $x - (a - bi)$ if it has the factor $x - (a + bi)$.

Recall that a quadratic polynomial $ax^2 + bx + c$ over the field of real numbers has no real zeros if its discriminant $b^2 - 4ac < 0$. Thus real quadratic polynomials with negative discriminants are irreducible over the field of real numbers. Now regard a polynomial with real coefficients as a polynomial over the field of complex numbers. It then has a factorization into linear factors. Theorem 12 tells us that every linear factor corresponding to an imaginary zero can be paired with a linear factor corresponding to its conjugate zero, and that the product of two such linear factors is a real quadratic polynomial. Hence we have the following theorem.

Theorem 13. A polynomial over the field of real numbers can be written uniquely as the product of a real number times a product of real monic irreducible quadratic factors and real monic linear factors.

For a polynomial over the field of rational numbers, the following theorem gives us a means of determining its rational zeros. This theorem and its corollary are sometimes helpful in determining whether a polynomial over the field of rational numbers is reducible. We first note that multiplication by the proper integer replaces a polynomial with rational coefficients by an associate that has integral coefficients. Thus we reduce our problem to that of finding the rational zeros of a polynomial with integral coefficients.

Theorem 14. Let c/d, where $(c, d) = 1$, be a rational zero of the polynomial $a_0 + a_1x + \cdots + a_nx^n$ with integral coefficients. Then c divides a_0 and d divides a_n.

Now $a_0 + a_1(c/d) + \cdots + a_{n-1}(c/d)^{n-1} + a_n(c/d)^n = 0$, and hence the integer

(5) $\qquad a_0d^n + a_1cd^{n-1} + \cdots + a_{n-1}c^{n-1}d + a_nc^n = 0.$

Thus $d(a_0d^{n-1} + a_1cd^{n-2} + \cdots + a_{n-1}c^{n-1}) + a_nc^n = 0$, and d divides a_nc^n. However, $(c^n, d) = 1$ (see Exercise 7, p. 17), and hence d divides a_n. Similarly the integer (5) may be written $a_0d^n + c(a_1d^{n-1} + \cdots + a_nc^{n-1}) = 0$, and c divides a_0d^n, but again $(c, d^n) = 1$, and hence c divides a_0.

Corollary. All rational zeros of the polynomial $a_0 + a_1x + \cdots + a_{n-1}x^{n-1} + x^n$ with integral coefficients are integers and divisors of a_0.

The corollary follows from the theorem when we note that d divides $a_n = 1$.

We note that the above corollary gives us a simple way of proving that certain real numbers such as $\sqrt{3}$ and $\sqrt[3]{5}$ are irrational, for they are zeros respectively of the polynomials $x^2 - 3$ and $x^3 - 5$. It is easily checked that these polynomials have no rational zeros.

Example. Find the rational zeros and the decomposition of the polynomial $f(x) = 6x^4 - 7x^3 + 6x^2 - 1$ over the field of rational numbers. By the above theorem the possible rational zeros are ± 1, $\pm\frac{1}{2}$, $\pm\frac{1}{3}$, $\pm\frac{1}{6}$. Using synthetic division, we find that neither ± 1 are zeros but that $\frac{1}{2}$ is a zero:

$$
\begin{array}{rrrrr|l}
6 & -7 & 6 & 0 & -1 & \frac{1}{2} \\
  & 3 & -2 & 2 & 1 & \\
\hline
6 & -4 & 4 & 2 & 0. &
\end{array}
$$

As we now know that $f(x) = (x - \frac{1}{2})(6x^3 - 4x^2 + 4x + 2)$, we use the quotient divided by 2, namely $3x^3 - 2x^2 + 2x + 1$, to discover the remaining rational zeros of $f(x)$. Now it is necessary only to try $\pm\frac{1}{3}$. We find that $-\frac{1}{3}$ is a zero and that $3x^2 - 3x + 3$ is the second quotient. Since $x^2 - x + 1$ has no rational zeros, $6(x - \frac{1}{2})(x + \frac{1}{3})(x^2 - x + 1)$ is the decomposition of $f(x)$ over the field of rational numbers.

Exercises

1. Find the decomposition of the polynomial $x^4 + 9x^3 + 28x^2 + 36x + 16$ over the field of rational numbers.

2. Find the decomposition of the polynomial $4x^4 + 8x^3 + 7x^2 + 8x + 3$ over the field of rational numbers and over the field of complex numbers.

3. Find the decomposition of the polynomial $x^3 - 25x - 48$ over the field of rational numbers and over the field of real numbers.

4. Find the decomposition of $x^5 - 1$ over the field of complex numbers and over the field of real numbers.

5. Find the decompositions of $x^8 - 1$ and $x^{12} - 1$ over the field of complex numbers, over the field of real numbers, and over the field of rational numbers.

6. Find the decomposition over the field of residue classes modulo 5 of the polynomial $2x^3 + 3x^2 + 3x + 1$.

7. Find the greatest common divisor of $2x^4 + 9x^2 + 17x - 21$ and $x^3 + 2x^2 + 4x + 21$. Hence find the decomposition of the first polynomial over the field of real numbers and over the field of complex numbers.

6 · Relation between the zeros and coefficients of a polynomial

In any field F in which the polynomial

$$f(x) = a_0 + a_1x + \cdots + a_nx^n$$

over F has the decomposition

$$f(x) = a_n(x - r_1)(x - r_2) \cdots (x - r_n),$$

there are certain relations between the coefficients of the polynomial and its zeros which will be described below. The following functions of the zeros $r_1, r_2, \cdots, r_n$ are called the elementary symmetric functions of $r_1, r_2, \cdots, r_n$:

$$S_1 = r_1 + r_2 + \cdots + r_n = \Sigma r_1,$$

$$S_2 = r_1 r_2 + r_1 r_3 + \cdots + r_{n-1} r_n = \Sigma r_1 r_2,$$

$$\cdots\cdots\cdots\cdots\cdots\cdots\cdots\cdots\cdots$$

$$S_n = r_1 r_2 r_3 \cdots r_n.$$

Thus the jth elementary symmetric function is the sum of the products, consisting of j distinct factors each, that can be formed from the zeros $r_1, r_2, \cdots, r_n$. Thus there are $C(n, j) = n!/[(n - j)!\,j!]$ terms in the jth elementary symmetric function. These functions are called symmetric functions because they remain unchanged or invariant when they are operated on by the elements of the symmetric group on n symbols.

In order to obtain the desired relations we now prove the following lemma.

Lemma.

(6) $\quad (x - r_1)(x - r_2) \cdots (x - r_n) = x^n - S_1 x^{n-1}$
$$+ S_2 x^{n-2} + \cdots + (-1)^j S_j x^{n-j} + \cdots + (-1)^n S_n.$$

Note that, when $n = 1$, $x - r_1 = x - S_1$, and when $n = 2$,

$$(x - r_1)(x - r_2) = x^2 - (r_1 + r_2)x + r_1 r_2 = x^2 - S_1 x + S_2,$$

where the S's are the elementary symmetric functions of one and two variables respectively. We make the proof by induction. Assume the lemma true for $n = k$:

(7) $\quad (x - r_1)(x - r_2) \cdots (x - r_k) = x^k - S_1 x^{k-1}$
$$+ S_2 x^{k-2} + \cdots + (-1)^j S_j x^{k-j} + \cdots + (-1)^k S_k.$$

Here S_j is the jth elementary symmetric function of $r_1, r_2, \cdots, r_k$. Multiply both sides of equation (7) by $x - r_{k+1}$, obtaining

(8) $\quad (x - r_1)(x - r_2) \cdots (x - r_k)(x - r_{k+1}) =$
$$x^{k+1} - (S_1 + r_{k+1})x^k + (S_2 + r_{k+1}S_1)x^{k-1} + \cdots$$
$$+ (-1)^j (S_j + r_{k+1}S_{j-1})x^{k-j+1} + \cdots + (-1)^{k+1} r_{k+1} S_k.$$

Let $S_1', S_2', \cdots, S_{k+1}'$ be the elementary symmetric functions of

$r_1, r_2, \cdots, r_k, r_{k+1}$. Then $S_1' = S_1 + r_{k+1}$, $S_2' = S_2 + r_{k+1}S_1$, $\cdots$, $S_j' = S_j + r_{k+1}S_{j-1}$. For we note that the sum of the products of j distinct factors each of $r_1, r_2, \cdots, r_k, r_{k+1}$ is the sum of the products of j distinct factors each of $r_1, r_2, \cdots, r_k$ plus r_{k+1} times the sum of the products of $j - 1$ factors each of these zeros. Thus (8) is of the form (6) with $n = k + 1$, and the induction is complete.

Now

$$f(x) = a_0 + a_1x + \cdots + a_nx^n = a_n(x - r_1)(x - r_2) \cdots (x - r_n)$$

$$= a_n(x^n - S_1x^{n-1} + \cdots + (-1)^n S_n),$$

and, equating the first and the last forms of the polynomial, we have the following theorem.

Theorem 15. *If* $f(x) = a_0 + a_1x + \cdots + a_nx^n$ *over a field* F *has the* n *zeros* $r_1, r_2, \cdots, r_n$ *in* F, *then* $S_j = (-1)^j a_{n-j}/a_n$, $j = 1, 2, \cdots, n$.

Exercises

1. Using the relation between the zeros and the coefficients of a polynomial, find a polynomial over the field of rational numbers whose zeros are a) $-1, 2, 3$; b) $2, 2, 2$; c) $0, 0, 1, 2$; d) $-1, -1, 3, 4$.

2. Denote the zeros of the following polynomials by r_1, r_2, r_3, r_4. Find the values of their elementary symmetric functions for each of the polynomials:

   a) $x^4 + 4x^3 - 2x + 3$.
   b) $4x^4 + 4x^3 + x^2 - x + 2$.
   c) $3x^4 - 4x^2 + 2$.

3. If r_1, r_2, r_3 are the zeros of $x^3 - 3x^2 + 2x + 1$, find a polynomial whose zeros are $2r_1, 2r_2, 2r_3$.

4. Let r_1, r_2, r_3 be the zeros of the polynomial $2x^3 - 3x^2 + kx - 1$. Determine the constant k if the sum of two of them is 2. Find the zeros of the resulting polynomial.

5. Let r_1, r_2, r_3 be the zeros of the polynomial $\sqrt{2}\,x^3 + kx^2 - 2\sqrt{2}\,x + 2$. Determine the constant k if the product of two of the zeros is 1. Find the zeros of the resulting polynomial.

6. Determine k so that one zero of the polynomial $3x^3 - kx^2 - 7x + 3$ is the reciprocal of another. Hence determine the zeros of the polynomial.

7 · Derivative of a polynomial

We formally define the derivative of $f(x) = a_0 + a_1x + \cdots + a_nx^n$ to be $f'(x) = a_1 + 2a_2x + \cdots + na_nx^{n-1}$. Here, of course,

$2a_2$ means $a_2 + a_2$. This definition can be used to prove the usual formulas for the derivatives of sums, products, and powers of polynomials, and we shall use these formulas. We note, for example, that, if the polynomial is a polynomial over the field of complex numbers, the only polynomials whose derivatives are zero are the constants. However, if, for example, $f(x) = x^p$ is regarded as a polynomial over the field of residue classes modulo p, where p is a prime, $f(x)$ has the derivative px^{p-1}, which is zero. The results due to the use of derivatives depend upon whether the derivative of a polynomial is zero only when the polynomial is an element in a field or whether it may also be zero when the polynomial is of positive degree.   To avoid this complication we shall *restrict our field of coefficients to the field of complex numbers or to one of its subfields.* The interested student may read in more advanced texts what can be proved when this restriction is not made.

8 · Multiple factors

Definitions. If the polynomial $[p(x)]^m$ divides the polynomial $f(x)$ and if no higher power of $p(x)$ divides $f(x)$, $p(x)$ is said to be a factor of multiplicity m of $f(x)$. If $(x - a)^m$ divides the polynomial $f(x)$ and if no higher power of $x - a$ divides $f(x)$, a is called a zero of multiplicity m.

In the following theorems we shall restrict the field of coefficients of the polynomial $f(x)$ to the field of complex numbers or one of its subfields.

Theorem 16.   Let $p(x)$ be an irreducible factor of $f(x)$ of multiplicity $m > 1$. Then $[p(x)]^{m-1}$ is the highest power of $p(x)$ that occurs as a factor of the greatest common divisor of $f(x)$ and its derivative $f'(x)$. Conversely, if the greatest common divisor of $f(x)$ and $f'(x)$ has the irreducible factor $p(x)$ as a factor of multiplicity $m - 1$, $p(x)$ is an irreducible factor of $f(x)$ of multiplicity m.

First, let $p(x)$ be an irreducible factor of multiplicity m of $f(x)$. Then we may write $f(x) = [p(x)]^m q(x)$, where $p(x)$ and $q(x)$ are relatively prime, for $f(x)$ has a unique factorization into irreducible polynomials.   Now the derivative

$$f'(x) = [p(x)]^{m-1}[m \, p'(x) \cdot q(x) + p(x) \cdot q'(x)].$$

It is obvious that $[p(x)]^{m-1}$ is a common factor of $f(x)$ and $f'(x)$

and hence that it divides their g.c.d. We show that no higher power of $p(x)$ occurs as a factor of the g.c.d. by proving that $m - 1$ is the highest power of $p(x)$ that divides $f'(x)$. Now $p(x)$ is relatively prime to its derivative $p'(x)$, because $p'(x)$ is of degree less than the degree of $p(x)$ and hence it can have no factor in common with the irreducible polynomial $p(x)$. Thus $p(x)$ does not divide the second factor of $f'(x)$, for it is relatively prime to $p'(x) \cdot q(x)$ and divides $p(x) \cdot q'(x)$. Hence $m - 1$ is the highest power of $p(x)$ that divides the g.c.d. of $f(x)$ and $f'(x)$.

It remains to prove the converse. Now let the g.c.d. of $f(x)$ and $f'(x)$ have the irreducible factor $p(x)$ of multiplicity $m - 1$. Let k be the highest power of $p(x)$ that divides $f(x)$. Using the unique factorization theorem, we again have $f(x) = [p(x)]^k q(x)$, where $p(x)$ and $q(x)$ are relatively prime polynomials. By the above proof the g.c.d. of $f(x)$ and $f'(x)$ has $p(x)$ as an irreducible factor of multiplicity $k - 1$. Hence $k - 1 = m - 1$ and $k = m$, as was to be proved.

Corollary 1. A polynomial f(x) *has no repeated factor of multiplicity greater than* 1 *if and only if it and its derivative are relatively prime.*

This corollary is easily seen to be true when we consider that any factor of $f(x)$ can be decomposed into its irreducible factors.

Corollary 2. If r *is a zero of multiplicity* m *of the g.c.d. of* f(x) *and its derivative, then* r *is a zero of multiplicity* m + 1 *of* f(x).

This corollary is immediate from the theorem, for a zero of a polynomial corresponds to an irreducible linear factor of the polynomial.

To show that this theorem cannot be applied to a polynomial over any field of coefficients, we consider the polynomial $f(x) = x^3 - 1$ over the field of residue classes modulo 3. We see that $x^3 - 1 = (x - 1)^3$ and hence has an irreducible factor of multiplicity 3. However, $f'(x) = 3x^2 = 0$.

Example. Determine whether the polynomial $f(x) = x^4 + 2x^3 - 2x - 1$ has any irreducible factors of multiplicity greater than 1. If it has, find them and hence find the decomposition of the polynomial over the field of rational numbers.

Now $f'(x) = 4x^3 + 6x^2 - 2$, and $4f(x) = f'(x) \cdot (x + \frac{1}{2}) - 3(x^2 + 2x + 1)$. The g.c.d. of $f(x)$ and $f'(x)$ divides $(x + 1)^2$, the monic remainder when $4f(x)$ is divided by $f'(x)$. Hence, if an irreducible factor of multiplicity greater than 1 of $f(x)$ exists, it must be $x + 1$. By synthetic division we find that $f'(x) = 2(x + 1)^2(2x - 1)$. Thus $f(x)$ has the factor $x + 1$ as a factor of multiplicity 3, and by synthetic division we find that $f(x) = (x + 1)^3(x - 1)$. At any stage in the greatest common divisor process the student should simplify his work by observing what possible factors the remainder has.

Exercises

1. Determine whether the following polynomials have zeros of multiplicity greater than 1. If zeros of multiplicity greater than 1 exist, find all the zeros of the polynomial.

    a) $x^4 - 4x^3 + 5x^2 - 4x + 4$.   b) $x^4 + 2x^3 - x^2 - 4x - 2$.
    c) $x^3 - 7x^2 + 15x - 9$.   d) $8x^4 - 4x^3 - 6x^2 + 5x - 1$.

2. Find the decomposition of the following polynomials over the field of rational numbers, the field of real numbers, and the field of complex numbers:

    a) $x^5 - x^4 + 2x^3 - 2x^2 + x - 1$.   b) $x^6 - 2x^4 - 4x^2 + 8$.

3. Show that the following polynomials have no repeated factors:

    a) $x^n - a$, $a \neq 0$.   b) $x^6 - 6x + 1$.
    c) $x^5 + x^4 - 4x^3 + 4$.   d) $x^6 - 6x^3 + 1$.

4. Find the condition that the coefficients must satisfy if the following polynomials have no repeated factors:

    a) $ax^2 + bx + c$, $a \neq 0$.   b) $x^3 + 3ax + b$.

5. For what real values of a has the polynomial $x^n + nax + n - 1$, where $n > 1$, a repeated factor?

9 · Taylor's theorem for the polynomial

Theorem 17. Let $f(x)$ *be a polynomial of degree* n. *Then*
$f(x + h) = f(h) + xf'(h) + x^2f''(h)/2 + \cdots + x^k f^{(k)}(h)/k! + \cdots + x^n f^{(n)}(h)/n!.$

The polynomial $f(x + h)$ may be expressed as a polynomial in x whose coefficients are functions of h and of the coefficients of $f(x)$. Thus let

$$f(x + h) = b_0 + b_1 x + b_2 x^2 + \cdots + b_k x^k + \cdots + b_n x^n.$$

Its successive derivatives are:

$$f'(x + h) = b_1 + 2b_2 x + 3b_3 x^2 + \cdots + kb_k x^{k-1} + \cdots + nb_n x^{n-1},$$

$$f''(x + h) = 2b_2 + 3 \cdot 2b_3 x + \cdots + k(k - 1)b_k x^{k-2} + \cdots + n(n - 1)b_n x^{n-2},$$

$$\cdots \cdots \cdots \cdots \cdots \cdots \cdots \cdots \cdots \cdots \cdots \cdots \cdots \cdots \cdots$$

$$f^{(k)}(x + h) = k! b_k + \cdots + n(n - 1) \cdots (n - k + 1)b_n x^{n-k},$$

$$\cdots \cdots \cdots \cdots \cdots \cdots \cdots \cdots \cdots \cdots \cdots \cdots \cdots \cdots \cdots$$

$$f^{(n)}(x + h) = n! b_n.$$

For $x = 0$, we have $f(h) = b_0$, $f'(h) = b_1$, $f''(h) = 2b_2$, $\cdots$, $f^{(k)}(h) = k! b_k$, $\cdots$, $f^{(n)}(h) = n! b_n$. Substituting these values of b_i in $f(x + h)$, we have the desired result

$$f(x + h) = f(h) + xf'(h) + x^2 \frac{f''(h)}{2} + \cdots + x^n \frac{f^{(n)}(h)}{n!}.$$

This is one form of Taylor's theorem for the polynomial. If in it we replace x by $x - h$, we have

$$f(x) = f(h) + (x - h)f'(h) + (x - h)^2 \frac{f''(h)}{2} + \cdots + (x - h)^k \frac{f^{(k)}(h)}{k!} + \cdots + (x - h)^n \frac{f^{(n)}(h)}{n!}.$$

This second form indicates how we can easily calculate the values of $f(h)$, $f'(h)$, $f''(h)/2$, $\cdots$, $f^{(n)}(h)/n!$. Using this second form of Taylor's theorem, we see that when $f(x)$ is divided by $x - h$ the remainder is $f(h)$ and the quotient is

$$f'(h) + (x - h)\frac{f''(h)}{2} + \cdots + (x - h)^{n-1} \frac{f^{(n)}(h)}{n!}.$$

If this quotient is divided by $x - h$, the remainder is $f'(h)$. We can continue in this fashion, dividing the successive quotients by $x - h$, and obtain the desired coefficients $f''(h)/2$, $\cdots$, $f^{(n)}(h)/n!$. The student should recall that the simplest method of dividing a polynomial by $x - h$ is synthetic division.

Consider the relation between the zeros of $f(x)$ and those of $f(x + h)$. Let x_1 be a zero of $f(x)$. Thus $x_1 - h$ is a zero of

$f(x + h)$, for $f(x_1 - h + h) = f(x_1) = 0$. Thus each zero of $f(x + h)$ is h less than the corresponding zero of $f(x)$.

Theorem 18. A polynomial f(x) *has the number* a *as a zero of multiplicity* m *if and only if* f(a) = 0, f′(a) = 0, $\cdots$, f$^{(m-1)}$(a) = 0, *and* f$^{(m)}$(a) $\neq$ 0.

If a is a zero of multiplicity m of $f(x)$, then $f(x)$ is divisible by $(x - a)^m$ and no higher power of $x - a$. Write

$$f(x) = f(a) + (x - a)f'(a) + (x - a)^2\frac{f''(a)}{2} + \cdots$$

$$+ (x - a)^n\frac{f^{(n)}(a)}{n!}.$$

Hence we see that if a is a zero of multiplicity m, it is necessary that $f(a) = 0$, $f'(a) = 0$, $\cdots$, $f^{(m-1)}(a) = 0$, but that $f^{(m)}(a) \neq 0$. Conversely, if $f(a) = 0$, $f'(a) = 0$, $\cdots$, $f^{(m-1)}(a) = 0$ but if $f^{(m)}(a) \neq 0$, $f(x)$ is exactly divisible by $(x - a)^m$ and by no higher power of $x - a$.

Exercises

1. Express the polynomial $x^3 + 2x - 5$ as a polynomial in $x - 3$ and as a polynomial in $x + 2$.
2. Find the polynomial each of whose zeros is 3 less than the zeros of $x^4 - x^2 + 2x - 1$.
3. Find the polynomial each of whose zeros is 2 greater than the zeros of the polynomial $3x^3 - 4x^2 + 2$.
4. Show that the polynomial $8x^4 + 84x^3 + 114x^2 + 55x + 9$ has a zero of multiplicity 3.

Matrices over a Field

1 · Matrix notation

In solving systems of simultaneous linear equations, the student soon realizes that the coefficients play the important role in finding solutions. The "unknowns" merely act as marks of position. For this reason new notations were introduced to simplify the writing of a system of equations.   For example, the system

$$a_{11}x_1 + a_{12}x_2 + \cdots + a_{1n}x_n = c_1,$$
$$a_{21}x_1 + a_{22}x_2 + \cdots + a_{2n}x_n = c_2,$$
$$\dots\dots\dots\dots\dots\dots\dots\dots\dots\dots\dots$$
$$a_{m1}x_1 + a_{m2}x_2 + \cdots + a_{mn}x_n = c_m$$

might be denoted as follows:

$$
\begin{bmatrix}
a_{11} & a_{12} & \cdots & a_{1n} \\
a_{21} & a_{22} & \cdots & a_{2n} \\
\dots & \dots & \dots & \dots \\
a_{m1} & a_{m2} & \cdots & a_{mn}
\end{bmatrix}
\begin{bmatrix}
x_1 \\ x_2 \\ \cdot \\ x_n
\end{bmatrix}
=
\begin{bmatrix}
c_1 \\ c_2 \\ \cdot \\ c_m
\end{bmatrix}.
$$

Here we have a rectangular array of the a_{ij} arranged in m rows and n columns, a column of n unknowns x_j, and a column of m constants c_i.   Such a notation leads us to the study of rectangular arrays of elements called matrices.   We shall restrict our study to matrices with elements in a field.

Definition.   An m by n matrix A over a field F is a rectangular array of mn elements a_{ij} in F arranged in m rows and n columns, thus:

$$A = \begin{bmatrix} a_{11} & a_{12} & \cdots & a_{1n} \\ a_{21} & a_{22} & \cdots & a_{2n} \\ \cdots\cdots\cdots\cdots\cdots \\ a_{m1} & a_{m2} & \cdots & a_{mn} \end{bmatrix}.$$

It is customary to enclose the array with brackets, parentheses, or double straight lines on each side of the array. We shall use the above notation. The elements a_{i1}, a_{i2}, $\cdots$, a_{in} are the elements of the ith row, whereas the elements a_{1k}, a_{2k}, $\cdots$, a_{mk} are the elements of the kth column. Thus the first subscript indicates the row in which the element lies, while the second subscript indicates the column in which it lies. A single row $[a_{i1}\ a_{i2} \cdots a_{in}]$ is itself a 1 by n (or, as we shall write it, $1 \times n$) matrix, whereas a single column

$$\begin{bmatrix} a_{1k} \\ a_{2k} \\ \cdot \\ \cdot \\ \cdot \\ a_{mk} \end{bmatrix}$$

is an $m \times 1$ matrix. These are often spoken of as row and column matrices or *vectors*. To save space the matrix A is often simply written

$$[a_{ij}], \qquad i = 1, 2, \cdots, m;\ j = 1, 2, \cdots, n.$$

If $m = n$, the matrix is called a square matrix.

2 · Addition and multiplication

Before we define operations on matrices we must define equality of two matrices. Two $m \times n$ matrices $A = [a_{ij}]$ and $B = [b_{ij}]$ are equal if and only if $a_{ij} = b_{ij}$ for all i and j. In other words, two matrices are equal if and only if they are identical. We shall now define some operations on matrices, and we shall note that sum and product are defined only under certain conditions.

Sum. The sum $A + B$ of the two $m \times n$ matrices A and B is the $m \times n$ matrix $C = [c_{ij}]$, where $c_{ij} = a_{ij} + b_{ij}$. Thus to add two matrices of the same dimensions we merely add elements in corresponding positions. Note that the sum of matrices of different dimensions is not defined. Moreover, as addition in a field is commutative and associative, we see that the addition of matrices also obeys these laws.

Multiplication by a scalar. A scalar is an element in the field F. The word is used to distinguish it from a matrix composed of the elements of the field. Let b be an element of the field F, or in other words a scalar, and let A be the $m \times n$ matrix $[a_{ij}]$. We define $bA = [ba_{ij}]$ and $Ab = [a_{ij}b]$. Since multiplication in a field is commutative, $bA = Ab$. Thus, when a matrix is multiplied by an element in the field, the result is a matrix in which each element of the original matrix is multiplied by the given element.

Matrix multiplication. The product AB of two matrices A and B is defined only if the number of columns in A is equal to the number of rows in B. Let $A = [a_{ij}]$ and $B = [b_{jk}]$, with $i = 1$, $2, \cdots, m$, with $j = 1, 2, \cdots, n$, and with $k = 1, 2, \cdots, p$. Then $AB = [c_{ik}]$, where

$$c_{ik} = a_{i1}b_{1k} + a_{i2}b_{2k} + \cdots + a_{in}b_{nk} = \sum_{j=1}^{n} a_{ij}b_{jk}.$$

Thus, to obtain the element in the ith row and the kth column of the product AB, form a sum from the products of the elements of the ith row of A and the elements of the kth column of B. Note that the product of an $m \times n$ matrix times an $n \times p$ matrix is an $m \times p$ matrix.

Examples.

1. Let $A = \begin{bmatrix} a_{11} & a_{12} & a_{13} \\ a_{21} & a_{22} & a_{23} \end{bmatrix}$ and $B = \begin{bmatrix} b_{11} & b_{12} & b_{13} \\ b_{21} & b_{22} & b_{23} \\ b_{31} & b_{32} & b_{33} \end{bmatrix}$;

then

$$AB = \begin{bmatrix} a_{11}b_{11}+a_{12}b_{21}+a_{13}b_{31} & a_{11}b_{12}+a_{12}b_{22}+a_{13}b_{32} & a_{11}b_{13}+a_{12}b_{23}+a_{13}b_{33} \\ a_{21}b_{11}+a_{22}b_{21}+a_{23}b_{31} & a_{21}b_{12}+a_{22}b_{22}+a_{23}b_{32} & a_{21}b_{13}+a_{22}b_{23}+a_{23}b_{33} \end{bmatrix}.$$

2. Let $A = \begin{bmatrix} 1 & 2 \\ 3 & 1 \\ -1 & 2 \end{bmatrix}$ and $B = \begin{bmatrix} 1 & 2 & 3 \\ 4 & 0 & 1 \end{bmatrix}$;

then

$$AB = \begin{bmatrix} 1(1) + 2(4) & 1(2) + 2(0) & 1(3) + 2(1) \\ 3(1) + 1(4) & 3(2) + 1(0) & 3(3) + 1(1) \\ (-1)(1) + 2(4) & (-1)(2) + 2(0) & (-1)(3) + 2(1) \end{bmatrix}$$

$$= \begin{bmatrix} 9 & 2 & 5 \\ 7 & 6 & 10 \\ 7 & -2 & -1 \end{bmatrix}.$$

In Exercise 3 below, the student will see that matrix multiplication is not commutative. We shall prove that the associative and distributive laws hold if the matrices involved are of the proper dimensions.

Associative law for multiplication. Let $A = [a_{ij}]$, with $i = 1$, $2, \cdots, m$, and with $j = 1, 2, \cdots, n$; let $B = [b_{jk}]$, with $k = 1, 2, \cdots, p$; and let $C = [c_{kr}]$, with $r = 1, 2, \cdots, q$. Then $AB = [d_{ik}]$, where $d_{ik} = \sum_{j=1}^{n} a_{ij}b_{jk}$; and $(AB)C = [e_{ir}]$, where $e_{ir} = \sum_{k=1}^{p} d_{ik}c_{kr} = \sum_{k=1}^{p} \sum_{j=1}^{n} a_{ij}b_{jk}c_{kr}$.

Now $BC = [f_{jr}]$, where $f_{jr} = \sum_{k=1}^{p} b_{jk}c_{kr}$; and $A(BC) = [g_{ir}]$, where $g_{ir} = \sum_{j=1}^{n} a_{ij}f_{jr} = \sum_{j=1}^{n} a_{ij} \sum_{k=1}^{p} b_{jk}c_{kr} = \sum_{j=1}^{n} \sum_{k=1}^{p} a_{ij}b_{jk}c_{kr} = e_{ir}$.

The summations may be interchanged, for these are sums in a field.

Distributive laws. Let A and B be the above matrices, and $C = [c_{jk}]$, with $j = 1, 2, \cdots, n$, and with $k = 1, 2, \cdots, p$. We prove that $A(B + C) = AB + AC$. Note that, if B is an $n \times p$ matrix, C must also be an $n \times p$ matrix in order that the addition may be performed. Now $B + C = [b_{jk} + c_{jk}] = [g_{jk}]$, and $A(B + C) = [h_{ik}]$, where $h_{ik} = \sum_{j=1}^{n} a_{ij}g_{jk} = \sum_{j=1}^{n} a_{ij}(b_{jk} + c_{jk}) = \sum_{j=1}^{n} a_{ij}b_{jk} + \sum_{j=1}^{n} a_{ij}c_{jk} = d_{ik} + s_{ik}$. But $[d_{ik}] = AB$, and $[s_{ik}] = AC$. Thus $A(B + C) = AB + AC$. It is left to the student to prove the second distributive law $(B + C)A = BA + CA$, where, of course, the matrices must be chosen with the proper dimensions.

Exercises

1. Perform the following matrix multiplications:

a) $\begin{bmatrix} 1 & 2 & -1 \\ 3 & 2 & 4 \\ 2 & 1 & 3 \end{bmatrix} \begin{bmatrix} 1 & 0 \\ 3 & -1 \\ 0 & 0 \end{bmatrix}$.   b) $[1 \quad 2 \quad 3] \begin{bmatrix} 2 & -1 & 4 \\ 0 & 1 & 5 \\ 2 & 3 & 0 \end{bmatrix}$.

2. If $A = \begin{bmatrix} 1 & -1 \\ 0 & 2 \end{bmatrix}$, $B = \begin{bmatrix} 1 & 3 & 0 \\ 2 & 0 & 1 \end{bmatrix}$, and $C = \begin{bmatrix} 2 \\ 3 \\ -1 \end{bmatrix}$, show by computation that $(AB)C = A(BC)$.

3. If $A = \begin{bmatrix} 2 & -1 \\ 0 & 1 \end{bmatrix}$ and $B = \begin{bmatrix} 1 & 0 \\ -1 & -1 \end{bmatrix}$, show that $(A + B)(A + B) = A^2 + AB + BA + B^2 \neq A^2 + 2AB + B^2$.

4. If $A = \begin{bmatrix} 0 & i \\ -i & 0 \end{bmatrix}$, find A^2, A^3, A^4.

5. If $A = \begin{bmatrix} 0 & 1 \\ 1 & 0 \end{bmatrix}$ and $B = \begin{bmatrix} 0 & 0 \\ 1 & 0 \end{bmatrix}$, find AB, A^2, B^2, B^2A, and $2A + 3B$.

6. If $A = [a_{ij}]$ is a 4×3 matrix, and if $B = [b_{jk}]$ is a 3×4 matrix, find the element in the third row and second column of AB.

7. If the dimensions of the matrices A, B, C are properly chosen, prove that $(A + B) + C = A + (B + C)$.

8. If the dimensions of the matrices A, B, C are properly chosen, prove that $(B + C)A = BA + CA$.

9. Let $B = [b_{ij}]$ be an $m \times n$ matrix and let A be the $n \times n$ matrix $[a_{jk}]$, with $a_{jj} = a$, and with $a_{jk} = 0$ when $j \neq k$. Prove that $BA = Ba$.

3 · Matrix multiplication and systems of linear equations

We return to the system of equations given on p. 90. Now that matrix multiplication has been defined, we see that the system of equations can be written $AX = C$, if we denote the $m \times n$ matrix $[a_{ij}]$ by A, the matrix $\begin{bmatrix} x_1 \\ x_2 \\ \cdot \\ \cdot \\ \cdot \\ x_n \end{bmatrix}$ by X, and the matrix $\begin{bmatrix} c_1 \\ c_2 \\ \cdot \\ \cdot \\ \cdot \\ c_m \end{bmatrix}$ by C.

Consider the set of equations

$$x' = x \cos \theta_1 - y \sin \theta_1,$$

(1)

$$y' = x \sin \theta_1 + y \cos \theta_1.$$

These equations may be regarded as transforming the point (x, y) in the plane into the point (x', y') in the plane. The point (x', y') is obtained from the point (x, y) by rotating the plane about the origin of the coordinate system through an angle θ_1, the rotation being a counterclockwise rotation when $\theta_1 > 0$. This set of equations may be given by the matrix equation

$$\begin{bmatrix} x' \\ y' \end{bmatrix} = \begin{bmatrix} \cos \theta_1 & -\sin \theta_1 \\ \sin \theta_1 & \cos \theta_1 \end{bmatrix} \begin{bmatrix} x \\ y \end{bmatrix},$$

which we shall abbreviate as $X' = AX$. Suppose now that it is desired to make a second counterclockwise rotation of the plane through an angle θ_2. This rotation will carry the point (x', y') into a third point (x'', y''), and the relation between the coordinates is given by

$$x'' = x' \cos \theta_2 - y' \sin \theta_2,$$

(2)

$$y'' = x' \sin \theta_2 + y' \cos \theta_2.$$

It is geometrically obvious that these two rotations carried out successively carry the point (x, y) into the point (x'', y''). The relations between the coordinates x, y and the coordinates x'', y'' are

$$x'' = x \cos (\theta_1 + \theta_2) - y \sin (\theta_1 + \theta_2),$$

(3)

$$y'' = x \sin (\theta_1 + \theta_2) + y \cos (\theta_1 + \theta_2).$$

We see that we can obtain equations (3) by eliminating x' and y' from equations (1) and (2). This elimination is most easily accomplished by writing equations (1) and (2) in matrix form thus: $X' = AX$, $X'' = BX'$. Then it is easily seen that $X'' = BX' = B(AX) = (BA)X$. The student should check that, if equations (3) are written in the matrix form $X'' = CX$, the matrix $C = BA$.

In general, if the set of m linear equations

$$x_1' = a_{11}x_1 + a_{12}x_2 + \cdots + a_{1n}x_n,$$

$$x_2' = a_{21}x_1 + a_{22}x_2 + \cdots + a_{2n}x_n,$$

$$\dots\dots\dots\dots\dots\dots\dots\dots\dots\dots\dots\dots$$

$$x_m' = a_{m1}x_1 + a_{m2}x_2 + \cdots + a_{mn}x_n$$

express the m variables x_i' as linear functions of the n variables x_j, and if a second set of p linear equations

$$x_1'' = b_{11}x_1' + b_{12}x_2' + \cdots + b_{1m}x_m',$$

$$x_2'' = b_{21}x_1' + b_{22}x_2' + \cdots + b_{2m}x_m',$$

$$\cdots\cdots\cdots\cdots\cdots\cdots\cdots\cdots\cdots\cdots$$

$$x_p'' = b_{p1}x_1' + b_{p2}x_2' + \cdots + b_{pm}x_m'$$

express the p variables x_k'' as linear functions of the m variables x_i', then the variables x_k'' may be expressed as linear functions of the variables x_i. This computation can be done most easily by means of matrices. Let $A = [a_{ij}]$, with $i = 1, 2, \cdots, m$, and $j = 1, 2, \cdots, n$; $B = [b_{ki}]$, with $k = 1, 2, \cdots, p$, and $i = 1, 2,$

$$\cdots, m;\quad X = \begin{bmatrix} x_1 \\ x_2 \\ \cdot \\ \cdot \\ \cdot \\ x_n \end{bmatrix}; \; X' = \begin{bmatrix} x_1' \\ x_2' \\ \cdot \\ \cdot \\ \cdot \\ x_m' \end{bmatrix}; \text{ and } X'' = \begin{bmatrix} x_1'' \\ x_2'' \\ \cdot \\ \cdot \\ \cdot \\ x_p'' \end{bmatrix}.$$

We can then write the above two systems of equations as $X' = AX$ and $X'' = BX'$. Thus $X'' = BX' = B(AX) = (BA)X$, and we have the desired result. The student thus sees a reason for defining matrix multiplication in the particular way it was done.

Exercises

1. Given $x_1' = 2x_1 - 3x_2$, $x_2' = x_1 + x_2$, $x_1'' = 3x_1' - 4x_2'$, and $x_2'' = x_1' - x_2'$, express the variables x_1'' and x_2'' as linear functions of x_1 and x_2. Make the computation by means of matrices and write the final result as a system of equations.

2. Given $x_1' = x_1 - x_2 + x_3$, $x_2' = x_1 + x_2$, $x_1'' = 2x_1' + x_2'$, and $x_2'' = 3x_1' - x_2'$, express the variables x_1'' and x_2'' as linear functions of x_1, x_2, and x_3. Make the computation by means of matrices and write the final result as a system of equations.

4 · Special matrices

Zero matrix. The $m \times n$ matrix each of whose elements is the zero element of the field is called a zero matrix. Note that, if A is an $m \times n$ zero matrix and if B is an $n \times p$ matrix, the product

AB is an $m \times p$ zero matrix. The student's attention is called to the fact that the product of two matrices A and B may be a zero matrix although neither A nor B is a zero matrix. (See the matrix B^2 in Exercise 5, p. 94.)

Identity matrix. An $m \times m$ matrix $I = [e_{ij}]$ is called the $m \times m$ identity matrix if $e_{ij} = 0$, $i \neq j$, and if $e_{ii} = 1$, the unity element of the field. Now let $B = [b_{jk}]$ be an $m \times p$ matrix. Then the element in the ith row and kth column of IB is $\sum_{j=1}^{m} e_{ij}b_{jk} = e_{ii}b_{ik} = b_{ik}$. Thus $IB = B$. Moreover, if B is an $m \times m$ matrix, then $BI = B$. Thus the $m \times m$ identity matrix I is commutative with every $m \times m$ matrix.

Scalar matrix. An $m \times m$ matrix $A = [a_{ij}]$, where $a_{ij} = 0$, $i \neq j$, and $a_{ii} = a$, is called a scalar matrix. If B is any $m \times p$ matrix, it is left to the student to prove that $AB = aB$. Thus multiplication of a matrix by a scalar matrix produces the same result as multiplying a matrix by a scalar. Note that the identity matrix is a special case of a scalar matrix.

Transpose of a matrix. Let $A = [a_{ij}]$ be an $m \times n$ matrix. The transpose A' of A is defined as follows: $A' = [a_{ji}']$, where $a_{ji}' = a_{ij}$. Thus the jth row of the transpose A' of A is the jth column of A. If A is an $m \times n$ matrix, A' is an $n \times m$ matrix.

For example, if $A = \begin{bmatrix} 1 & 2 & -1 \\ 3 & 2 & 0 \end{bmatrix}$, $A' = \begin{bmatrix} 1 & 3 \\ 2 & 2 \\ -1 & 0 \end{bmatrix}$.

Theorem 1. The following laws govern transposes of sums and products of matrices: $(A + B)' = A' + B'$; $(aA)' = aA'$, *where* a *is a scalar; and* $(AB)' = B'A'$.

The proofs of the first two laws will be left to the student as exercises. We shall prove the product law. Let $A = [a_{ij}]$ be an $m \times n$ matrix, and let $B = [b_{jk}]$ be an $n \times p$ matrix. Then $B' = [b_{kj}']$ and $A' = [a_{ji}']$. Therefore $B'A' = [c_{ki}']$, where $c_{ki}' = \sum_{j=1}^{n} b_{kj}'a_{ji}'$. Since $b_{kj}' = b_{jk}$ and $a_{ji}' = a_{ij}$, we have $c_{ki}' = \sum_{j=1}^{n} b_{jk}a_{ij} = c_{ik}$. However, $AB = [c_{ik}]$ and $(AB)' = [c_{ki}']$.

Exercises

1. Letting $A = \begin{bmatrix} 1 & -3 & 2 \\ 1 & 2 & 1 \end{bmatrix}$ and $B = \begin{bmatrix} 1 \\ 2 \\ 1 \end{bmatrix}$, find $(AB)'$ in two ways.

2. Letting $A = \begin{bmatrix} 3 & -1 & 0 \\ 2 & 1 & 1 \end{bmatrix}$, find $2A$, $2A'$, and $(2A)'$.

3. Letting $A = \begin{bmatrix} 3 & -1 \\ 2 & 4 \\ 1 & 2 \end{bmatrix}$ and $B = \begin{bmatrix} 0 & 1 \\ 2 & -1 \\ 0 & 0 \end{bmatrix}$, find $(A + B)'$ and $A' + B'$.

4. Prove that $(aA)' = aA'$, where a is a scalar.
5. Prove that $(A + B)' = A' + B'$.
6. Prove that $(A')' = A$.

5 · Partitioning of matrices

Let $A = [a_{ij}]$ be an $m \times n$ matrix. The $r \times s$ array of elements obtained from A by deleting any $m - r$ rows and any $n - s$ columns of A is called a submatrix of A. The matrix A may be partitioned into submatrices in many ways. For example, the matrix A may be partitioned as follows: $A = \begin{bmatrix} A_1 & A_2 \\ A_3 & A_4 \end{bmatrix}$,

where $A_1 = \begin{bmatrix} a_{11} & \cdots & a_{1s} \\ \cdots & \cdots & \cdots \\ a_{r1} & \cdots & a_{rs} \end{bmatrix}$, $A_2 = \begin{bmatrix} a_{1,\,s+1} & \cdots & a_{1n} \\ \cdots & \cdots & \cdots \\ a_{r,\,s+1} & \cdots & a_{rn} \end{bmatrix}$,

$A_3 = \begin{bmatrix} a_{r+1,\,1} & \cdots & a_{r+1,\,s} \\ \cdots & \cdots & \cdots \\ a_{m1} & \cdots & a_{ms} \end{bmatrix}$, and $A_4 = \begin{bmatrix} a_{r+1,\,s+1} & \cdots & a_{r+1,\,n} \\ \cdots & \cdots & \cdots \\ a_{m,\,s+1} & \cdots & a_{mn} \end{bmatrix}$.

Here A_1 is an $r \times s$ matrix, A_2 an $r \times (n - s)$ matrix, A_3 an $(m - r) \times s$ matrix, and A_4 an $(m - r) \times (n - s)$ matrix. Sometimes, in order to facilitate the multiplication of two matrices, it is useful to partition both matrices so that the multiplication can be carried out by using submatrices. Thus, if we wish to obtain the matrix AB, where $B = [b_{jk}]$ is an $n \times p$ matrix, it might be useful to partition A as indicated above. Then, B must be partitioned so that it is possible to carry out the submatrix multiplication. For example, B may be partitioned to become a 2×1 matrix whose elements are the submatrices B_1 and B_2,

thus: $B = \begin{bmatrix} B_1 \\ B_2 \end{bmatrix}$, where B_1 is an $s \times p$ matrix and B_2 an

$(n - s) \times p$ matrix. With this partitioning perform the multiplication AB by using the submatrices A_i and B_j as elements.

Thus, $AB = \begin{bmatrix} A_1B_1 + A_2B_2 \\ A_3B_1 + A_4B_2 \end{bmatrix}$, a 2×1 matrix with matrices as

elements. It is necessary, of course, to prove that this product actually equals the usual product AB, when the multiplication rule for elements is used. We shall illustrate the proof. For example, the element in the rth row and the tth column of AB is

$\sum_{j=1}^{n} a_{rj}b_{jt}$ by definition. Moreover, it is the element in the rth row and tth column of $A_1B_1 + A_2B_2$, for we may write this element

as $\sum_{j=1}^{s} a_{rj}b_{jt} + \sum_{j=s+1}^{n} a_{rj}b_{jt}$. Similarly any other element of AB may be written so that it is seen to belong to either one of the two submatrices of AB.

Example. Let $A = \begin{bmatrix} 0 & 0 & \vdots & 1 & 2 \\ 0 & 0 & \vdots & 1 & -1 \end{bmatrix} = [A_1 \quad A_2]$ and $B =$

$\begin{bmatrix} 1 & 2 \\ 3 & 4 \\ \cdots \\ 1 & 0 \\ 0 & 1 \end{bmatrix} = \begin{bmatrix} B_1 \\ B_2 \end{bmatrix}$, the partitioning being denoted by the dotted

lines. Then $AB = [A_1B_1 + A_2B_2] = [0 + A_2B_2] = [A_2B_2] = \begin{bmatrix} 1 & 2 \\ 1 & -1 \end{bmatrix}$.

6 · Row equivalence

The student will recall that the first method he encountered in solving systems of simultaneous linear equations was the method of elimination. Thus to solve the system of equations

(4)
$$3x - y = 6,$$
$$x + 2y = 2$$

the student might multiply the first equation by 2, add the second equation to the first, obtaining $7x = 14$, and then divide by 7, finally obtaining the equation $x = 2$ in place of the first equation. He might now replace the second equation with one found by subtracting $x = 2$ from the second equation, obtaining $2y = 0$ and finally $y = 0$. Thus the process of solving (4) was to find the simpler pair of equations $x = 2$, $y = 0$. It is necessary to prove, of course, that the values of x and y given by the final set satisfy the original equations and that no other values of x and y satisfy the original pair. This question of the equivalence of the two sets of equations will be discussed later.

The student's attention now will be directed to the essential manipulation involved in the method. Note that, if the equations (4) are written in matrix form

$$(5) \qquad \begin{bmatrix} 3 & -1 \\ 1 & 2 \end{bmatrix} \begin{bmatrix} x \\ y \end{bmatrix} = \begin{bmatrix} 6 \\ 2 \end{bmatrix},$$

the operations performed on the equations (4) are essentially operations performed on the rows of the matrices $\begin{bmatrix} 3 & -1 \\ 1 & 2 \end{bmatrix}$ and $\begin{bmatrix} 6 \\ 2 \end{bmatrix}$. The first operation, namely the multiplication of the first equation by 2, replaces the equation (5) by

$$(6) \qquad \begin{bmatrix} 6 & -2 \\ 1 & 2 \end{bmatrix} \begin{bmatrix} x \\ y \end{bmatrix} = \begin{bmatrix} 12 \\ 2 \end{bmatrix}.$$

The second operation, namely the addition of the second equation of (4) to the first equation of (4), replaces the matrix equation (6) by

$$(7) \qquad \begin{bmatrix} 7 & 0 \\ 1 & 2 \end{bmatrix} \begin{bmatrix} x \\ y \end{bmatrix} = \begin{bmatrix} 14 \\ 2 \end{bmatrix}.$$

Continuing in this fashion, we successively obtain

$$\begin{bmatrix} 1 & 0 \\ 1 & 2 \end{bmatrix} \begin{bmatrix} x \\ y \end{bmatrix} = \begin{bmatrix} 2 \\ 2 \end{bmatrix}, \begin{bmatrix} 1 & 0 \\ 0 & 2 \end{bmatrix} \begin{bmatrix} x \\ y \end{bmatrix} = \begin{bmatrix} 2 \\ 0 \end{bmatrix}, \text{ and } \begin{bmatrix} 1 & 0 \\ 0 & 1 \end{bmatrix} \begin{bmatrix} x \\ y \end{bmatrix} = \begin{bmatrix} 2 \\ 0 \end{bmatrix}.$$

Performing the matrix multiplication in the last matrix equation, we have $\begin{bmatrix} x \\ y \end{bmatrix} = \begin{bmatrix} 2 \\ 0 \end{bmatrix}$, which gives us the final two linear equations.

Such operations on the rows of a matrix lead us to ask the question: exactly what is the form that a matrix will finally assume if we perform such operations on its rows? This question brings us to a more precise definition of these row operations.

Elementary row operations. Let $A = [a_{ij}]$ be an $m \times n$ matrix. Denote the ith row of A by A_i. The elementary row operations on the matrix A are:

1) the interchange of any two rows; i.e., the row A_k of A may be replaced by the row A_j of A and the row A_j by A_k;

2) the multiplication of a row by an element $c \neq 0$ of the field; i.e., the row A_k may be replaced by the row cA_k, if $c \neq 0$;

3) the addition of one row to another; i.e., the row A_k may be replaced by the row $A_j + A_k$.

Definition. An $m \times n$ matrix B is said to be row equivalent to an $m \times n$ matrix A if B can be obtained from A by a finite number of elementary row operations. We write $B \cong A$.

It is easily seen that row equivalence is a true equivalence relation. It is obvious that A is row equivalent to A, for we may regard having obtained A from A by using row operation 2) with $c = 1$, the unity element of the field. Moreover, if B is row equivalent to A, A is row equivalent to B. For, if B had been obtained from A by elementary row operation 1), the same elementary row operation performed on B would give A; if B had been obtained from A by row operation 2), A could be obtained from B by using a similar row operation with c replaced by $1/c$; finally, if B had been obtained from A by row operation 3), A could be obtained from B by adding -1 times the jth row to the kth row. Thus each elementary row operation has an inverse that is either an elementary row operation or a combination of elementary row operations. Finally, the transitive property is obvious, for if B can be obtained from A and if C can be obtained from B, then C can be obtained from A by elementary row operations.

Modified triangular form of a matrix. A matrix is said to be in modified triangular form if a) the first nonzero element in each row is 1, the unity element of the field, if b) in each row after the first the number of zeros preceding this first nonzero element exceeds the number of zeros preceding the first nonzero element of the previous row, if c), when the first nonzero element in the ith row lies in the jth column, all other elements in the jth column are zero, and if d) the first row has a nonzero element.

Example.
$$\begin{bmatrix} 0 & 1 & 3 & 0 \\ 0 & 0 & 0 & 1 \\ 0 & 0 & 0 & 0 \end{bmatrix}.$$

Theorem 2. An m $\times$ n *matrix is row equivalent to an* m $\times$ n *matrix in modified triangular form.*

Either every element in the first column of the given matrix A is zero, or there exists an element x that is not zero in the kth row, say, of this column. In the latter case, interchange the first and kth rows of A. Then x appears in the first row and first column of the resulting matrix, and it can be replaced by 1 by multiplying the first row of the matrix by x^{-1}. The remaining elements of the first column can then be made zero by adding proper multiples of the first row to the other rows. Thus A is row equivalent to a matrix in either of the forms $[0 \quad C]$ or $\begin{bmatrix} 1 & D \\ 0 & E \end{bmatrix}$, where in the first case 0 represents the $m \times 1$ zero matrix and C an $m \times (n-1)$ matrix, whereas in the second case 0 represents the $(m-1) \times 1$ zero matrix, D a $1 \times (n-1)$ matrix, and E an $(m-1) \times (n-1)$ matrix. In the first case repeat the above process with the matrix C, whereas in the second case repeat the process with the matrix E. If in the latter case E has been replaced by a matrix with 1 in the first row and column, a proper multiple of this row in the whole matrix can be added to the first row to make the first element of D zero without changing the first column of the whole matrix. Thus in all cases a continuation of the process leads to the desired form.

Elementary matrices. An $m \times m$ matrix obtained from the $m \times m$ identity matrix I by means of one elementary row operation on I is called an elementary matrix. Thus there are three types of elementary matrices corresponding to the three elementary row operations. These types will now be described. Denote the ith row of a matrix A by the one-rowed matrix A_i. Thus a matrix is completely determined by giving its rows. Let P, Q, and R be the matrices obtained from I by performing elementary row operations 1), 2), and 3) respectively on I. Then these elementary matrices may be described as follows:

$$P \text{ with } P_i = I_i, \, i \neq j, \, k, \, P_j = I_k, \, P_k = I_j;$$

$$Q \text{ with } Q_i = I_i, \, i \neq k, \, Q_k = cI_k, \, c \neq 0;$$

$$R \text{ with } R_i = I_i, \, i \neq k, \, R_k = I_j + I_k.$$

Examples.

$$P = \begin{bmatrix} 1 & 0 & 0 \\ 0 & 0 & 1 \\ 0 & 1 & 0 \end{bmatrix}; \, Q = \begin{bmatrix} 1 & 0 & 0 \\ 0 & c & 0 \\ 0 & 0 & 1 \end{bmatrix}; \, R = \begin{bmatrix} 1 & 0 & 0 \\ 0 & 1 & 1 \\ 0 & 0 & 1 \end{bmatrix}.$$

$$j = 2, \, k = 3. \qquad\qquad k = 2. \qquad\qquad j = 3, \, k = 2.$$

Theorem 3. *Each elementary row operation on an* m $\times$ n *matrix A can be effected by premultiplication of A by an elementary matrix.*

To interchange the jth and kth rows of A, we form the product PA. Let $[PA]_i$ denote the ith row of PA. Recall that the ith row of PA is obtained by multiplying the ith row of P by each column of A. Thus $[PA]_i = P_iA = I_iA = A_i$ when $i \neq j, \, k$; $[PA]_j = P_jA = I_kA = A_k$; and $[PA]_k = P_kA = I_jA = A_j$. The student can easily check that the matrix QA is the matrix obtained from A by means of row operation 2). Similarly RA is the matrix obtained from A by performing row operation 3) on A, for we have $[RA]_i = R_iA = I_iA = A_i$ when $i \neq k$, and $[RA]_k = R_kA = (I_j + I_k)A = I_jA + I_kA = A_j + A_k$.

Corollary. *If an* m $\times$ n *matrix B is row equivalent to an* m $\times$ n *matrix A, then B = SA, where S is a product of elementary matrices.*

Exercises

1. Find matrices in modified triangular form row equivalent to

a) $\begin{bmatrix} 1 & 2 & -1 & 4 \\ 3 & 2 & 0 & 2 \\ 0 & 1 & 3 & 2 \\ 3 & 3 & 3 & 4 \end{bmatrix}$;   b) $\begin{bmatrix} 1 & 2 \\ 3 & 4 \\ -1 & 2 \\ 1 & 1 \end{bmatrix}.$

2. Let I be the $m \times m$ identity matrix and let A be an $m \times n$ matrix. Prove that a) $I_i A = A_i$ and b) $(I_j + I_k)A = A_j + A_k$.

3. We are given the matrix $A = \begin{bmatrix} 2 & -1 & 4 \\ 3 & 3 & 6 \end{bmatrix}$. In each of the following cases exhibit the matrix E such that EA is a) the matrix obtained from A by interchanging the two rows, b) the matrix obtained from A by dividing the second row by 2, c) the matrix obtained from A by adding the first row to the second.

4. If $A = \begin{bmatrix} 1 & 2 \\ 0 & 1 \\ 2 & 1 \end{bmatrix}$, exhibit the elementary matrix E such that $EA = \begin{bmatrix} 2 & 1 \\ 0 & 1 \\ 1 & 2 \end{bmatrix}$ and the elementary matrix F such that $FA = \begin{bmatrix} 1 & 2 \\ 0 & 1 \\ 2 & 2 \end{bmatrix}$.

5. If $A = \begin{bmatrix} 1 & 3 & -1 \\ 2 & 2 & 0 \end{bmatrix}$, exhibit the product of the elementary matrices that reduce it to a row equivalent modified triangular form.

6. Show that $\begin{bmatrix} 1 & 2 & 1 \\ 3 & 1 & 2 \\ 0 & 1 & 2 \end{bmatrix}$ is row equivalent to the 3×3 identity matrix.

7 · Nonsingular matrices

Definition. A square matrix A is said to be *nonsingular* if a matrix B exists such that $BA = AB = I$. If B exists, it will be denoted by A^{-1} and it is called the inverse of A. If A^{-1} does not exist, the matrix A is said to be *singular*.

Theorem 4. The inverse of a nonsingular matrix is unique.

Let $BA = AB = I$, and let $CA = AC = I$. Then $BA = CA$, $(BA)B = (CA)B$, $B(AB) = C(AB)$, $BI = CI$, and $B = C$.

Theorem 5. If A and B are nonsingular matrices, then the product AB is a nonsingular matrix. Moreover, $(AB)^{-1} = B^{-1}A^{-1}$.

Now B^{-1} and A^{-1} exist. Hence $(B^{-1}A^{-1})(AB) = B^{-1}[A^{-1}(AB)] = B^{-1}[(A^{-1}A)B] = B^{-1}(IB) = B^{-1}B = I$. Similarly $(AB)(B^{-1}A^{-1}) = I$. Thus AB is nonsingular, and $B^{-1}A^{-1}$ is its inverse.

Theorem 6. The elementary matrices P, Q, R *are nonsingular.*

Since $PP = I$, P is its own inverse. The matrices Q^{-1} and R^{-1} are described by exhibiting their rows: $Q_i^{-1} = I_i$ when $i \neq k$, and $Q_k^{-1} = c^{-1}I_k$; $R_i^{-1} = I_i$ when $i \neq k$, and $R_k^{-1} = I_k - I_j$.

Since the product of nonsingular matrices is nonsingular, a product of elementary matrices is nonsingular. Hence the above corollary becomes

Theorem 7. If a matrix B *is row equivalent to a matrix* A, *then* B = SA, *where* S *is nonsingular.*

Theorem 8. An n × n *matrix* A *is row equivalent to the identity matrix if and only if it is nonsingular.*

First, let A be nonsingular. Find a matrix B in modified triangular form row equivalent to A. Then $B = SA$, where S is a nonsingular matrix. Hence B is nonsingular, for the product of nonsingular matrices is nonsingular, and B^{-1} exists. We shall show that B cannot have a zero in its principal diagonal; i.e., if the element in the ith row and jth column of B is denoted by b_{ij}, then $b_{kk} \neq 0$ for all k. Recall that at least $j - 1$ zeros precede the first nonzero element in the jth row of B. Hence if $b_{kk} = 0$, the $(k + 1)$st row of B has at least $k + 1$ zeros preceding its first nonzero element. If $k = n$, the nth row of B consists of zeros, and, if $k < n$, at least one row of B after the kth consists of zeros. Consequently, if $b_{kk} = 0$, B has a row of zeros. Then $BB^{-1} = I$ has a row of zeros, contrary to the definition of I. Thus $b_{ii} = 1$ and $b_{ij} = 0$ when $i \neq j$. Thus B is the identity matrix, and hence A is row equivalent to the identity matrix.

Second, let A be row equivalent to the identity matrix I. Then $I = SA$, where S is nonsingular, and hence $A = S^{-1}I$ is nonsingular.

Theorem 9. If a square matrix is reduced to the identity matrix by a sequence of row operations, the same sequence of row operations performed on the identity produces the inverse of the given matrix.

Let A be the given matrix and let E_i denote elementary matrices. (Note that we are not using the notation for a row of a matrix here.) Now we are given $(E_s \cdots E_2 E_1)A = I$. Hence

$(E_s \cdots E_2 E_1)(AA^{-1}) = IA^{-1}$, giving $(E_s \cdots E_2 E_1)I = A^{-1}$, the desired result.

Example.   Find the inverse of the matrix $A = \begin{bmatrix} 1 & -2 \\ 1 & 1 \end{bmatrix}$.

Now, performing a single row operation at a time, we exhibit the successive matrices row equivalent to A in the left-hand column and the successive matrices row equivalent to I in the right-hand column:

$$\begin{bmatrix} 0 & -3 \\ 1 & 1 \end{bmatrix} \qquad \begin{bmatrix} 1 & -1 \\ 0 & 1 \end{bmatrix}$$

$$\begin{bmatrix} 0 & 1 \\ 1 & 1 \end{bmatrix} \qquad \begin{bmatrix} -\frac{1}{3} & \frac{1}{3} \\ 0 & 1 \end{bmatrix}$$

$$\begin{bmatrix} 0 & 1 \\ 1 & 0 \end{bmatrix} \qquad \begin{bmatrix} -\frac{1}{3} & \frac{1}{3} \\ \frac{1}{3} & \frac{2}{3} \end{bmatrix}$$

$$\begin{bmatrix} 1 & 0 \\ 0 & 1 \end{bmatrix} \qquad \begin{bmatrix} \frac{1}{3} & \frac{2}{3} \\ -\frac{1}{3} & \frac{1}{3} \end{bmatrix} = A^{-1}.$$

Combining the results of the preceding three theorems, we now have the following two corollaries.

Corollary 1.   A matrix is nonsingular if and only if it can be written as a product of elementary matrices.

Corollary 2.   A matrix B *is row equivalent to a matrix* A *if and only if* B = SA, *where* S *is a nonsingular matrix.*

Exercises

1. Prove: If A is a nonsingular matrix, then its transpose A' is a nonsingular matrix.

2. Find the inverses of the following matrices over the field of rational numbers and over the field of residue classes modulo 5:

a) $\begin{bmatrix} 1 & -3 & 2 \\ 2 & 0 & 0 \\ 1 & 4 & 1 \end{bmatrix}$.   b) $\begin{bmatrix} 2 & 4 & 3 \\ 0 & 1 & 1 \\ 2 & 2 & -1 \end{bmatrix}$.

3. Find the inverse of the matrix over the field of complex numbers:

$$\begin{bmatrix} i & -1 & 2i \\ 2 & 0 & 2 \\ -1 & 0 & 1 \end{bmatrix}.$$

4. Has the following matrix an inverse over the field of rational numbers?

$$\begin{bmatrix} 2 & 1 & 3 & 1 \\ 1 & 2 & -1 & 4 \\ 3 & 3 & 2 & 5 \\ 1 & -1 & 4 & -3 \end{bmatrix}.$$

5. Prove Corollary 1 and Corollary 2.

8 · Column equivalence

If in the definition of an elementary row operation on a matrix, the word row is replaced by the word column, we have the definition of an elementary column operation on a matrix. Similarly, the definition of column equivalence of two matrices can be read from the definition of row equivalence of two matrices by replacing the word row by the word column. An elementary column operation on a matrix A becomes an elementary row operation on the transpose A' of A. Let B be obtained from A by an elementary column operation. Then B' can be obtained from A' by an elementary row operation. Thus $B' = EA'$, where E is an elementary matrix, and consequently $B = AE'$. Hence we have the following theorem.

Theorem 10. An elementary column operation on an m × n *matrix* A *can be effected by multiplying* A *on the right by an* n × n *matrix obtained from the* n × n *identity matrix by the same elementary column operation.*

Similarly, if B is column equivalent to a matrix A, B' is row equivalent to A', $B' = SA'$, and $B = AS'$, where S' is nonsingular. Conversely, if $B = AT$, where T is nonsingular, $B' = T'A'$, so that B' is row equivalent to A', and consequently B is column equivalent to A. Hence we have the following theorem.

Theorem 11. An m × n *matrix* B *is column equivalent to an* m $\times$ n *matrix* A *if and only if* B = AT, *where* T *is an* n $\times$ n *nonsingular matrix.*

9 · Equivalence of matrices

Now both row and column operations may be applied to a matrix. If an $m \times n$ matrix B can be obtained from an $m \times n$ matrix A by a finite number of elementary row and column operations, the matrix B is said to be equivalent to the matrix A. Thus row and column equivalence are special cases of the general concept of equivalence of matrices. Combining our previous results, we have the following theorem, which is often used as a definition of the equivalence of two matrices.

Theorem 12. An m $\times$ n *matrix* B *is equivalent to an* m $\times$ n *matrix* A *if and only if* B = SAT, *where* S *and* T *are* m $\times$ m *and* n $\times$ n *nonsingular matrices respectively.*

Theorem 13. Canonical form. Every nonzero m $\times$ n *matrix* A *is equivalent to an* m $\times$ n *matrix of the form* $\begin{bmatrix} I & 0 \\ 0 & 0 \end{bmatrix}$, *where* I *is the* r $\times$ r *identity matrix, and where the remaining submatrices are zero matrices.*

Let some element a of A be different from zero. By performing elementary row and column operations on A, we obtain an equivalent matrix with the element a in the first row and the first column. Multiply the first row of this matrix by a^{-1}. Then by subtracting suitable multiples of the first row from the remaining rows and suitable multiples of the first column from the remaining columns, we obtain an equivalent matrix of the form $B = \begin{bmatrix} 1 & 0 \\ 0 & C \end{bmatrix}$, where C is an $(m - 1) \times (n - 1)$ submatrix and where the other submatrices are the 1×1 identity matrix and the $1 \times (n - 1)$ and the $(m - 1) \times 1$ zero matrices. The canonical form can now be established by an induction on m. If $m = 1$, then B is in canonical form. Assume the theorem true for all $(m - 1) \times (n - 1)$ matrices. Hence the submatrix C of B is equivalent to a matrix D in canonical form. Consequently B is equivalent to a matrix in canonical form, for the row and column operations performed on C to obtain D may be performed on the last $m - 1$ rows and the last $n - 1$ columns of B.

Exercises

1. Given the matrix $A = \begin{bmatrix} 1 & 2 & 3 \\ 0 & 1 & 2 \end{bmatrix}$, find nonsingular matrices T and U such that $AT = \begin{bmatrix} 2 & 1 & 3 \\ 1 & 0 & 2 \end{bmatrix}$ and $AU = \begin{bmatrix} 1 & 2 & 5 \\ 0 & 1 & 3 \end{bmatrix}$.

2. Find the canonical forms of the matrices in Exercise 1, p. 103 and in Exercise 4, p. 107.

3. Using Theorem 12 as the definition of equivalence of two matrices, prove that the equivalence of matrices is a true equivalence relation.

Two questions arise concerning the canonical form of a matrix: Is it unique? What determines the dimension of its identity submatrix? To answer these questions we introduce the concept of linear dependence and independence of the rows of a matrix over a field.

10 · Linear independence and dependence over a field

Definition. A set of p rows A_i, with $i = 1, 2, \cdots, p$, of an $m \times n$ matrix A, is linearly independent over a field F if and only if for all elements c_i of F the matrix equation

$$c_1 A_1 + c_2 A_2 + \cdots + c_p A_p = 0$$

implies $c_1 = c_2 = \cdots = c_p = 0$. A set of rows that is not linearly independent over F is said to be linearly dependent over F. Thus a set of p rows A_i of a matrix A is linearly dependent over F if there exist in F elements c_i, not all zero, such that $c_1 A_1 + c_2 A_2 + \cdots + c_p A_p = 0$.

As an example of a set of rows that is linearly independent, let us take the three rows of the 3×3 identity matrix. Here $c_1 I_1 + c_2 I_2 + c_3 I_3 = [c_1\ c_2\ c_3]$, which is the zero matrix if and only if $c_1 = c_2 = c_3 = 0$. The rows of the matrix $A = \begin{bmatrix} 2 & 0 \\ \sqrt{2} & 0 \end{bmatrix}$ are linearly dependent over the field of real numbers, for $A_1 - \sqrt{2} A_2 = [0\ 0]$ but they are linearly independent over the field of rational numbers, for $c_1 A_1 + c_2 A_2 = [2c_1 + \sqrt{2} c_2\ 0]$, and there are no nonzero rational numbers such that $2c_1 + \sqrt{2} c_2 = 0$.

Theorem 14.   *If* p *rows* A_i *of a matrix* A *are linearly independent over a field* F, *then any subset of* r $<$ p *of these rows is linearly independent over* F.

This is self-evident when we note that a linear combination $c_1A_1 + c_2A_2 + \cdots + c_rA_r$ of a subset of r of the given p rows $A_1, A_2, \cdots, A_p$ of A is also a linear combination of these p rows, the missing rows having the coefficient zero.

Theorem 15.   *A zero row* A_k *of a matrix* A *is always linearly dependent over a field* F.

Note that $cA_k = 0$, for all c in F.

Theorem 16.   *If a set of* p *nonzero rows* A_i, *with* i $= 1, 2, \cdots,$ p *of a matrix* A, *is linearly dependent over a field* F, *then there exists a maximum subset of* r $<$ p *rows which is linearly independent over* F.   *The remaining* p $-$ r *rows are linear combinations of these* r.

Since $A_1 \neq 0$, A_1 is linearly independent over F, for $c_1A_1 = 0$ implies $c_1 = 0$.   Now let $A_1, A_2, \cdots, A_r$, where $r \geq 1$, be linearly independent over F, and let A_j be any other one of the p rows under consideration.   Then $A_1, A_2, \cdots, A_r, A_j$ are either linearly dependent or linearly independent over F.   If they are linearly independent, we have not found a maximum subset of linearly independent rows, and so we would augment our set of linearly independent rows until we have found a maximum subset.   Hence assume that the r rows in question form a maximum subset of linearly independent rows.   Thus $A_1, A_2, \cdots, A_r, A_j$ are linearly dependent, and there exist in F elements c_i, not all zero, such that $c_1A_1 + c_2A_2 + \cdots + c_rA_r + c_jA_j = 0$.   If $c_j = 0$, then $A_1, A_2, \cdots, A_r$ are linearly dependent contrary to hypothesis.   Thus $c_j \neq 0$, and we can solve the above equation for A_j as a linear combination of the r rows $A_1, A_2, \cdots, A_r$.   Since A_j is any row not in the set of r linearly independent rows, the theorem is proved.

It is obvious that, if throughout the definition and the theorems of this section we replace the word row by the word column, we have the definition and theorems of the linear dependence and independence of the columns of a matrix.   We shall use the concept of the linear dependence and independence of the columns of a matrix in the next section.

11 · Rank of a matrix

Row rank of a matrix. The maximum number r of linearly independent rows over a field F of an $m \times n$ matrix over F is called the row rank of the matrix.

Theorem 17. Row equivalent matrices have the same row rank.

Let A be an $m \times n$ matrix of row rank r, and let s be the row rank of a matrix B obtained from A by means of one elementary row operation. Note that if $r < m$, then any $r + 1$ rows of A are linearly dependent. We prove $s \le r$. Note that, if $r = m$, then $s \le m$, for there are at most m rows to consider. If B has been obtained from A by means of an elementary row operation of type 1), $s = r$, for B has the same set of rows as A. If B has been obtained from A by an elementary row operation of type 2), any $r + 1$ rows of B not containing cA_k are linearly dependent, for these are rows of A. Moreover, any $r + 1$ rows of B containing cA_k are linearly dependent, for the corresponding rows of A, say—$A_1, A_2, \cdots, A_r$, A_k—are linearly dependent. Thus there exist, in F, c_i, not all zero, such that $c_1 A_1 + c_2 A_2 + \cdots + c_r A_r + c_k A_k = 0$. Multiplication of this matrix equation by $c \neq 0$ gives the linear dependence of the rows $A_1, A_2, \cdots, A_r, cA_k$ of B. If B has been obtained by an elementary row operation of type 3), we again note that any $r + 1$ rows of B not containing the row $A_j + A_k$ are linearly dependent, for they are rows of A. Let any $r + 1$ rows of B containing $A_j + A_k$ be denoted by $A_1, A_2, \cdots, A_r, A_j + A_k$. Then, again, since any $r + 1$ rows of A are linearly dependent, there exist in F elements c_i, not all zero, and elements d_i, not all zero, such that $c_1 A_1 + \cdots + c_r A_r + c_j A_j = 0$ and $d_1 A_1 + \cdots + d_r A_r + d_k A_k = 0$. If $c_j = 0$ or if $d_k = 0$, then either $c_1 A_1 + \cdots + c_r A_r + c_j(A_j + A_k) = 0$ or $d_1 A_1 + \cdots + d_r A_r + d_k(A_j + A_k) = 0$, and we have the desired linear dependence, for not all the c_i or d_i are zero. If $c_j \neq 0$ and if $d_k \neq 0$, then $A_j = c_1' A_1 + \cdots + c_r' A_r$ and $A_k = d_1' A_1 + \cdots + d_r' A_r$. Adding, we have $A_j + A_k = f_1 A_1 + \cdots + f_r A_r$, and the set of rows under consideration is linearly dependent. Thus in all cases $s \le r$. Hence an elementary row operation on a matrix does not produce a matrix of greater rank. Since row equivalence is reflexive, we may obtain B from A by elementary row operations, and hence $r \le s$. Thus, finally, $r = s$.

Corollary 1. If a matrix A *has the row rank* r, *then* SA, *where* S *is a nonsingular matrix, has row rank* r.

This is obvious when we recall that SA is a matrix row equivalent to A.

Corollary 2. The row rank of an n $\times$ n *nonsingular matrix is* n.

We need merely recall that a nonsingular matrix is row equivalent to the identity matrix, and the rows of the identity matrix are obviously linearly independent.

Column rank of a matrix. The column rank of a matrix is the maximum number of linearly independent columns of the matrix. Obviously the preceding theorems on the row rank of a matrix can be translated into corresponding theorems on the column rank of a matrix. Thus we have the following two theorems.

Theorem 18. Column equivalent matrices have the same column rank.

Theorem 19. If T *is a nonsingular matrix, the matrix* A *and the matrix* AT *have the same column rank.*

Theorem 20. The row rank of a matrix equals its column rank.

Let A be any nonzero matrix. There exist nonsingular matrices S and T such that $SAT = C$ is a matrix in canonical form. The row rank and the column rank of C are equal to r, the dimension of the identity submatrix of C. The row rank of A and SA is the same, say r_1. Thus the row rank of $CT^{-1} = SA$ is r_1, but CT^{-1} has at most r nonzero rows, for write $T^{-1} = \begin{bmatrix} T_1 \\ T_2 \end{bmatrix}$. Then $CT^{-1} =$

$$\begin{bmatrix} I & 0 \\ 0 & 0 \end{bmatrix} \begin{bmatrix} T_1 \\ T_2 \end{bmatrix} = \begin{bmatrix} IT_1 \\ 0 \end{bmatrix} = \begin{bmatrix} T_1 \\ 0 \end{bmatrix},$$ where T_1 is an r-rowed matrix.

Since T^{-1} is nonsingular, its rows are linearly independent, and thus the rows of T_1 are linearly independent. Hence CT^{-1} is of row rank r, and $r_1 = r$. Now consider the transpose $T'A'S' = C'$. The row ranks of $T'A'$ and A' are the same. Thus, as above, the row rank of $T'A' = C'S'^{-1}$ is r, and hence the column rank of AT and hence of A is r.

Thus the term the rank of a matrix can mean either the row or the column rank.

Theorem 21.   The canonical form of a matrix is unique.

In the preceding theorem we proved that the rank of A equals the rank of C.   If, now, there exist nonsingular matrices S_1 and T_1 such that $S_1 A T_1 = C_1$, a canonical form different from C, the rank of A equals the rank of C_1.   Hence the ranks of C and C_1 are equal, and hence the matrices C and C_1 are identical.

Theorem 22.   Two m $\times$ n *matrices are equivalent if and only if they have the same rank.*

Let the matrices A and B be equivalent.   In Theorem 20 we proved that the rank of A was the rank of its canonical form C. Since B is equivalent to A and since A is equivalent to C, B is equivalent to C.   Thus the rank of B is the rank of C, the canonical form of B.   Now let A and B be two $m \times n$ matrices of the same rank.   Each is equivalent to the same canonical form, for there is only one canonical form of rank r for an $m \times n$ matrix.   By the transitive property of equivalence, A is equivalent to B.

To determine the rank of a matrix it is often unnecessary to reduce it to its canonical form.   For example, the rank of a matrix can be read off from its modified triangular form.

Theorem 23.   The rank of a matrix in modified triangular form equals the number of its nonzero rows.

Let A be a matrix in modified triangular form, and let A_1, A_2, $\cdots$, A_r be its nonzero rows.   Its row rank and hence its rank is less than or equal to r, for any set of rows containing a zero row is obviously linearly dependent.   Then a linear relation $c_1 A_1 + c_2 A_2 + \cdots + c_r A_r = 0$ implies first that $c_1 = 0$; for, if the row A_1 contains its first nonzero element 1 in the kth position, the sum matrix $c_1 A_1 + \cdots + c_r A_r$ has c_1 in the kth position, and hence it must be zero if the sum matrix is the zero matrix.   Thus we have $c_2 A_2 + \cdots + c_r A_r = 0$, and by similar reasoning we have $c_2 = 0$, for, if A_2 has its first nonzero element 1 in the jth position, c_2 is the element in the jth position of the sum matrix.   Continuing in this fashion with the reduced equation $c_3 A_3 + \cdots + c_r A_r = 0$, we finally have $c_1 = c_2 = \cdots = c_r = 0$.

Exercises

1. Are the following pairs of matrices equivalent?   Why?

a) $\begin{bmatrix} 2 & -1 & 3 & 4 \\ 0 & 3 & 4 & 1 \\ 2 & 3 & 7 & 5 \\ 2 & 5 & 11 & 6 \end{bmatrix}$, $\begin{bmatrix} 1 & 0 & -5 & 6 \\ 3 & -2 & 1 & 2 \\ 5 & -2 & -9 & 14 \\ 4 & -2 & -4 & 8 \end{bmatrix}$.

b) $\begin{bmatrix} 4 & -1 & 2 \\ 3 & 4 & 0 \\ 1 & 0 & 0 \end{bmatrix}$, $\begin{bmatrix} 2 & 1 & 4 & 7 \\ 3 & 6 & 2 & 1 \\ 0 & 0 & 1 & 5 \end{bmatrix}$.

2. Determine the rank of each of the following matrices for rational values of the parameter k:

a) $\begin{bmatrix} 2 & 1 & -1 & 2 \\ 1 & 1 & 0 & 1 \\ k & 3 & -2 & 0 \\ 0 & 1 & -4 & 4 \end{bmatrix}$.   b) $\begin{bmatrix} k & 1 & 1 \\ 1 & k & 1 \\ 1 & 1 & k \end{bmatrix}$.

c) $\begin{bmatrix} 1 & 1 & -1 & 2 \\ k & 1 & 1 & 1 \\ 1 & -1 & 3 & -3 \\ 4 & 2 & 0 & k \end{bmatrix}$.

3. Are the m rows of an $m \times n$ matrix over a field F linearly dependent or linearly independent over F when $m > n$?   Why?

12 · Simultaneous linear equations over a field

We now apply the preceding matrix theory to the solution of m simultaneous linear equations in n unknowns $x_1, x_2, \cdots, x_n$ with coefficients and constant terms in a field F.   Write the system of equations

$$
\begin{aligned}
a_{11}x_1 + a_{12}x_2 + \cdots + a_{1n}x_n &= c_1, \\
a_{21}x_1 + a_{22}x_2 + \cdots + a_{2n}x_n &= c_2, \\
&\cdots\cdots\cdots\cdots\cdots \\
a_{m1}x_1 + a_{m2}x_2 + \cdots + a_{mn}x_n &= c_m
\end{aligned}
$$

(8)

in matrix form $AX = C$, where A is the $m \times n$ matrix $[a_{ij}]$, $X =$

$$\begin{bmatrix} x_1 \\ x_2 \\ \cdot \\ \cdot \\ \cdot \\ x_n \end{bmatrix}, \quad \text{and} \quad C = \begin{bmatrix} c_1 \\ c_2 \\ \cdot \\ \cdot \\ \cdot \\ c_m \end{bmatrix}.$$ The matrix A is called the matrix of

coefficients of the system of equations. The simplest case to solve is that in which the number of equations equals the number of unknowns and the matrix of coefficients is nonsingular.

Theorem 24. *The equation* $AX = C$, *with* $m = n$ *and* A *nonsingular, has the unique solution* $X = A^{-1}C$.

Since A is nonsingular, multiplication of $AX = C$ by A^{-1} gives $X = A^{-1}C$. Substituting this result in $AX = C$, we have $A(A^{-1}C) = IC = C$. It remains to prove that the solution is unique. Let X' be a second solution. Then $AX' = C$ implies $X' = A^{-1}C = X$.

We turn now to the case in which the relation between the number of unknowns and the number of equations is not restricted. Here we need consider the ranks of the matrix of coefficients and of the *augmented* matrix $A^* = [A\ C]$, which is an $m \times (n + 1)$ matrix obtained by augmenting A with the column of constants c_i, $i = 1, 2, \cdots, m$. We note that the rank of A^* is always greater than or equal to the rank of A, for A^* has at least as many linearly independent columns as A.

In the following lemma we show the relation between the solutions of the equation $AX = C$ and those of the equation $SAX = SC$, where S is a nonsingular matrix. Note that premultiplication by the nonsingular matrix S is equivalent to making row operations on A and C or to performing these operations on the linear equations (8).

Lemma. *If a solution* x_1', x_2', $\cdots$, x_n' *of the equation* $AX = C$ *exists, then it is also a solution of the equation* $SAX = SC$, *where* S *is a nonsingular matrix. Conversely, if* x_1', x_2', $\cdots$, x_n' *is a solution of the equation* $SAX = SC$, *where* S *is nonsingular, it is a solution of the equation* $AX = C$.

Let $X' = \begin{bmatrix} x_1' \\ x_2' \\ \cdot \\ \cdot \\ \cdot \\ x_n' \end{bmatrix}$ be a solution of $AX = C$; i.e., $AX' = C$ is an

identity. Then obviously $SAX' = SC$ is an identity. Conversely, if X' is a solution of $SAX = SC$, i.e., if $SAX' = SC$ is an identity, then $S^{-1}(SAX') = S^{-1}(SC)$ gives the identity $AX' = C$. Thus we have shown that all solutions of $AX = C$ are solutions of $SAX = SC$ and that no new solutions to the original equation $AX = C$ are introduced by multiplication by a nonsingular matrix.

Definition. If the system of equations (8) has a solution, the equations are said to be consistent. If the system has no solution, the equations are said to be inconsistent.

Theorem 25. The equation $AX = C$ *has a solution* X *if and only if the rank of* A, *the matrix of coefficients, equals the rank of the augmented matrix* A^*. *If* A *and* A^* *have the same rank, let* r *be their common rank. Then* r *of the unknowns may be expressed as linear functions of the constants* c_i *and the remaining* n − r *unknowns, to which may be assigned arbitrary values.*

Let A be of rank r. Reduce A to a row equivalent modified triangular form. Only the first r rows contain nonzero elements. Let the first nonzero elements in these r rows lie in the $k_1, k_2, \cdots,$ k_rth columns. These row operations on A may be effected by premultiplication by a nonsingular matrix S. Multiply each side of the equation $AX = C$ by S, obtaining $SAX = SC$. Now the last $m - r$ rows of SA are composed of zeros, and hence the last $m - r$ rows of SAX are composed of zeros. Thus, if the equation $AX = C$ is consistent, the last $m - r$ rows of SC are necessarily composed of zeros. Here we have a necessary and sufficient condition for the consistency of the system of equations (8). Now let the last $m - r$ rows of SC be composed of zeros, and let $b_1,$ $b_2, \cdots, b_r$ be the nonzero elements of SC. Further, let p_{ij} denote the element in the ith row and the jth column of SA. Then the matrix equation $SAX = SC$ gives us the following set of r

equations:

$$x_{k_1} + p_{1,k_1+1}x_{k_1+1} + \cdots + p_{1n}x_n = b_1,$$

where $p_{1k_j} = 0, j = 2, 3, \cdots, r$;

$$x_{k_2} + p_{2,k_2+1}x_{k_2+1} + \cdots + p_{2n}x_n = b_2,$$

where $p_{2k_j} = 0, j = 3, \cdots, r$;

$$\ldots\ldots\ldots\ldots\ldots\ldots\ldots\ldots\ldots\ldots$$

$$x_{k_r} + p_{r,k_r+1}x_{k_r+1} + \cdots + p_{rn}x_n = b_r.$$

Thus we have expressed the $x_{k_1}, x_{k_2}, \cdots, x_{k_r}$ as linear functions of the remaining x_j's and the constants b_i. The lemma tells us that this is a solution of the equation $AX = C$.

We interpret our results in terms of the ranks of the matrices A and A^*. Now SA and SA^* have the same ranks, respectively, as A and A^*. If SA and SA^* are of the same rank r, SA^* has $m - r$ zero rows, and hence the equations have a solution. If the equations have a solution, we have seen that SA^* has $m - r$ zero rows, and hence its rank is the same as SA. This reasoning is clear when we recall that SA^* is the matrix SA augmented by the column of b_i's. Thus the equation $AX = C$ has a solution if and only if A and A^* have the same rank.

Example. Solve the following system of equations:

$$x - y + 2z + w = 2,$$

$$3x + 2y + w = 1,$$

$$4x + y + 2z + 2w = 3.$$

Write the system in matrix form

$$\begin{bmatrix} 1 & -1 & 2 & 1 \\ 3 & 2 & 0 & 1 \\ 4 & 1 & 2 & 2 \end{bmatrix} \begin{bmatrix} x \\ y \\ z \\ w \end{bmatrix} = \begin{bmatrix} 2 \\ 1 \\ 3 \end{bmatrix}.$$

We reduce A^* to modified triangular form, thus simultaneously reducing A to modified triangular form.

$$A^* = \begin{bmatrix} 1 & -1 & 2 & 1 & 2 \\ 3 & 2 & 0 & 1 & 1 \\ 4 & 1 & 2 & 2 & 3 \end{bmatrix} \simeq \begin{bmatrix} 1 & 0 & \frac{4}{5} & \frac{3}{5} & 1 \\ 0 & 1 & -\frac{6}{5} & -\frac{2}{5} & -1 \\ 0 & 0 & 0 & 0 & 0 \end{bmatrix}.$$

Here the equations are consistent and the rank of A and A^* is 2. The matrix equation becomes

$$\begin{bmatrix} 1 & 0 & \frac{4}{5} & \frac{3}{5} \\ 0 & 1 & -\frac{6}{5} & -\frac{2}{5} \\ 0 & 0 & 0 & 0 \end{bmatrix} \begin{bmatrix} x \\ y \\ z \\ w \end{bmatrix} = \begin{bmatrix} 1 \\ -1 \\ 0 \end{bmatrix},$$

giving

$$x = -\tfrac{4}{5}z - \tfrac{3}{5}w + 1,$$
$$y = \tfrac{6}{5}z + \tfrac{2}{5}w - 1.$$

When these values for x and y are substituted in the original system of equations, they reduce to identities. Arbitrary values may be given to z and w, and thus this system of equations has an infinite number of solutions.

Exercises

Solve the following systems of equations. If a parameter k is involved, consider solutions for rational values of k.

1. $3x - 2y + z + 6 = 0,$
   $2x + 5y - 3z - 2 = 0,$
   $4x - 9y + 5z + 14 = 0.$

2. $4x + 7y - 14z = 10,$
   $2x + 3y - 4z = -4,$
   $x + y + z = 6.$

3. $4x - y + z = 5,$
   $2x - 3y + 5z = 1,$
   $x + y - 2z = 2,$
   $5x - z = 2.$

4. $2x - y - 2z = 0,$
   $x - 2y + z = 0,$
   $2x - 3y - z = 0.$

5. $kx - 3y - 5 = 0,$
   $8x + y - 17 = 0,$
   $kx + 2y - 10 = 0.$

6. $6x + 4y + 3z - 84w = 0,$
   $x + 2y + 3z - 48w = 0,$
   $x - 2y + z - 12w = 0,$
   $4x - 4y - z - 24w = 0.$

7. $x + y - z = 2,$
   $kx + y + z = 1,$
   $x - y + 3z = -3,$
   $4x + 2y = k.$

8. $x + y + 2z = 9,$
   $x + y - z = 0,$
   $2x - y + z = 3,$
   $x + 3y + 2z = 1.$

9. $x + y + 2w = 0,$
   $y + z = 0,$
   $x + z = 0,$
   $x + y + z + w = 0,$
   $x + y + 2z = 0.$

10. $x + ky + 3 = 0,$
    $kx + 3y + 1 = 0,$
    $kx + 4y - 6 = 0.$

11. $2x + y + 3z = 1,$
    $4x + 2y - z = -3,$
    $2kx + y - 4z = -4,$
    $10x + y - 6z = -10.$

12. $2x + y + 3z = 1,$
    $4x + 2y - z = -3,$
    $2kx + y - 4z = -4.$

13. $3x + y - z = 4,$
    $kx + y + z = 2,$
    $x + y - z = 1,$
    $x - z = k.$

14. $2x - y - 3z + 4w = 0,$
    $x + 3y + z - w = 0,$
    $4x + 5y - 2z + 6w = 0,$
    $3x - y - z - 7w = 0.$

13 Homogeneous linear equations

If, in the matrix equation $AX = C$, the matrix C is a zero matrix, the system of equations (8) is a set of homogeneous linear equations. We note that in this case the ranks of the augmented matrix and the matrix of coefficients are the same, so that there are always solutions of a set of homogeneous linear equations. Moreover, it is obvious that $(0, 0, \cdots, 0)$ is always a solution. The question of interest, then, is when do homogeneous linear equations have solutions other than $(0, 0, \cdots, 0)$, the trivial solution.

Theorem 26. A system of m *homogeneous linear equations in* n *unknowns has a solution other than* $(0, 0, \cdots, 0)$ *if and only if the rank of the matrix of coefficients is less than* n.

This is an obvious corollary of Theorem 25. If the rank of the matrix of coefficients is $r < n$, then $n - r > 0$, and r of the unknowns may be expressed as linear functions of the $n - r > 0$ unknowns. If $r = n$, the equation $SAX = 0$ shows that the n unknowns have only the value zero. Thus only if $r < n$ are there an infinite number of solutions other than $(0, 0, \cdots, 0)$.

The special case $m = n$ warrants attention.

Corollary. A system of n *homogeneous linear equations in* n *unknowns has a solution other than* $(0, 0, \cdots, 0)$ *if and only if the matrix of coefficients is singular.*

If the matrix of coefficients is singular its rank $< n$.

It may be of interest to note that the general solution of the equation $AX = C$ can be expressed as the sum of the general solution of the equation $AX = 0$ plus a particular solution of the equation $AX = C$, a particular solution of $AX = C$ being one in which the arbitrary parameters in the general solution are given particular values. In the illustrative example on p. 117, the general solution of the homogeneous system of equations

$$x - y + 2z + w = 0,$$

$$3x + 2y + w = 0,$$

$$4x + y + 2z + 2w = 0$$

is $x = -\frac{4}{5}z - \frac{3}{5}w$, $y = \frac{6}{5}z + \frac{2}{5}w$. A particular solution of the nonhomogeneous system is $z = 0$, $w = 0$, $x = 1$, $y = -1$.

14 · Linearly independent solutions of systems of linear equations

It is of interest to determine the number of linearly independent solutions of a consistent system $AX = C$ of m linear equations in n unknowns. We prove the following theorem.

Theorem 27. If a system of m *nonhomogeneous linear equations in* n *unknowns has a solution, it has exactly* n − r + 1 *linearly independent solutions, where* r *is the rank of the matrix of coefficients. A system of* m *homogeneous linear equations in* n *unknowns has exactly* n − r *linearly independent solutions,* r *being the rank of the matrix of coefficients.*

Let r be the rank of the matrix of coefficients and the augmented matrix of the system $AX = C$ of m linear equations in n unknowns. Then the solutions may be expressed as follows:

$$x_1 = \sum_{j=r+1}^{n} d_{1j}x_j + b_1,$$

(9)
$$x_2 = \sum_{j=r+1}^{n} d_{2j}x_j + b_2,$$

$$\cdots \cdots \cdots \cdots \cdots \cdots$$

$$x_r = \sum_{j=r+1}^{n} d_{rj}x_j + b_r.$$

Note that, if $r = n$, there is only the one solution $b_1, b_2, \cdots, b_n$.

If the equations are homogeneous, all the b's are zero. Thus the theorem holds for $r = n$. Now assume $r < n$. We form a matrix whose rows represent particular solutions of the equation $AX = C$. First let $x_j = 0, j = r + 1, \cdots, n$. Then one solution is $x_1 = b_1, x_2 = b_2, \cdots, x_r = b_r, x_j = 0, j = r + 1, \cdots, n$. In turn let $x_k = 1$, with $k \geq r + 1$, and let $x_j = 0$, with $k \neq j$ and $j \geq r + 1$. Thus we obtain $n - r + 1$ solutions. Let x_1', $x_2', \cdots, x_n'$ be any other solution. The matrix of these solutions is an $(n - r + 2) \times n$ matrix:

$$
\begin{bmatrix}
x_1' & x_2' & \cdots & x_r' & x_{r+1}' & x_{r+2}' \cdots x_n' \\
b_1 & b_2 & \cdots & b_r & 0 & 0 \cdots 0 \\
d_{1,r+1} + b_1 & d_{2,r+1} + b_2 & \cdots d_{r,r+1} + b_r & 1 & 0 \cdots 0 \\
d_{1,r+2} + b_1 & d_{2,r+2} + b_2 & \cdots d_{r,r+2} + b_r & 0 & 1 \cdots 0 \\
\cdots\cdots\cdots\cdots\cdots\cdots\cdots\cdots\cdots\cdots\cdots\cdots\cdots\cdots \\
d_{1n} + b_1 & d_{2n} + b_2 & \cdots & d_{rn} + b_r & 0 & 0 \cdots 1
\end{bmatrix}.
$$

Note that the last $n - r$ rows of this matrix are linearly independent, for their last $n - r$ columns form the $(n - r) \times (n - r)$ identity matrix. Thus the column rank of this $(n - r) \times n$ submatrix is $\geq n - r$, but its row rank is $\leq n - r$. Hence its rank is $n - r$ as stated. Further, if the b_i are not all zero, the last $n - r + 1$ rows are linearly independent, for these rows contain the $(n - r + 1) \times (n - r + 1)$ submatrix, consisting of the last $n - r$ columns and the column containing $b_k \neq 0$, whose columns are linearly independent. Thus, if the b_i are not all zero, we have exhibited a set of $n - r + 1$ linearly independent solutions. If the b_i are all zero, the equations are homogeneous, for, from (9), $(0, 0, \cdots, 0)$ is a solution. In this case we have exhibited a set of $n - r$ linearly independent solutions. It remains to prove that any other solution $x_1', x_2', \cdots, x_n'$ is a linear combination of the given set. To do this let R_i denote the ith row of the given matrix of solutions. Then

$$
R_1 - \sum_{j=r+1}^{n} x_j' (R_{j-r+2} - R_2) - R_2 = 0,
$$

for we need observe only that $x_1', x_2', \cdots, x_n'$ satisfy equations (9) by hypothesis. Thus any solution $x_1', x_2', \cdots, x_n'$ is a linear combination of the given set of linearly independent solutions.

Example.   In the example on p. 117 $n = 4$ and $r = 2$, so there exist 3 linearly independent solutions.   These may be taken to be $x = 1$, $y = -1$, $z = 0$, $w = 0$; $x = \frac{1}{5}$, $y = \frac{1}{5}$, $z = 1$, $w = 0$; and $x = \frac{2}{5}$, $y = -\frac{3}{5}$, $z = 0$, $w = 1$.

Exercises

1. Do m homogeneous linear equations in n unknowns have solutions other than $(0, 0, \cdots, 0)$ when $m < n$?   Why?

2. Exhibit a maximum set of linearly independent solutions for each of the following systems of equations:

a) $2x - 3y + 4z + w = 0,$
   $x + z - w = 0,$
   $3x - 3y + 5z = 0,$
   $4x - 3y + 6z - w = 0.$

b) $2x - 2y + 5z + 3w = 0,$
   $4x - y + z + w = 0,$
   $3x - 2y + 3z + 4w = 0,$
   $x - 3y + 7z + 6w = 0.$

c) $x + y - z = 2,$
   $3x + y + z = 1,$
   $x - y + 3z = -3,$
   $4x + 2y = 3.$

d) $2x + 3y - 4z + 5w = 2,$
   $3x + 5y - z + 2w = 1,$
   $7x + 11y - 9z + 12w = 5,$
   $3x + 4y - 11z + 13w = 5.$

7

Determinants and Matrices

1 · Definition

Just as we associate a real number $\sqrt{a^2 + b^2}$ with every complex number $a + bi$, we may associate with every square matrix over a field F an element of the field, known as the determinant of the matrix. Let $A = [a_{ij}]$ be an $n \times n$ matrix. Then the determinant of A is denoted by $|A| = |a_{ij}|$ and is defined as follows.

Determinant. The determinant $|A|$ of the $n \times n$ matrix $A = [a_{ij}]$ over the field F is the polynomial in the elements a_{ij} of the matrix A obtained in the following way. Take the product $a_{11}a_{22} \cdots a_{nn}$ of the elements in the principal diagonal of A, and operate on the row subscripts of the elements by the $n!$ permutations $p = \begin{pmatrix} 1 & 2 & \cdots & n \\ i_1 & i_2 & \cdots & i_n \end{pmatrix}$, where $i_1, i_2, \cdots, i_n$ are $1, 2, \cdots, n$ in some order, thus obtaining $n!$ distinct terms. If p is an even permutation, prefix a plus sign to the term; if p is an odd permutation, prefix a minus sign to the term. The sum of these $n!$ signed terms is the determinant $|A|$.

Let sgn p, read sign p, denote the plus sign if the permutation p is an even permutation and denote the minus sign if p is an odd permutation. Thus the term obtained from $a_{11}a_{22} \cdots a_{nn}$ by operating on the row subscripts of these elements by the permutation p may be written sgn $p\ a_{i_11}a_{i_22} \cdots a_{i_nn}$.

Example. Find the determinant of $A = \begin{bmatrix} a_{11} & a_{12} \\ a_{21} & a_{22} \end{bmatrix}$. The permutations on the symbols 1 and 2 are the identity $i = (1)(2)$ and $p = (12)$. Operating on the row subscripts of the elements in $a_{11}a_{22}$ by the identity, we obtain $a_{11}a_{22}$, and, since the identity

123

is an even permutation, this term is prefixed by a plus sign. Operating on the row subscripts of the elements in $a_{11}a_{22}$ by the permutation p, we obtain $a_{21}a_{12}$, and, since p is an odd permutation, this term is prefixed by a minus sign. Thus

$$\begin{vmatrix} a_{11} & a_{12} \\ a_{21} & a_{22} \end{vmatrix} = a_{11}a_{22} - a_{21}a_{12}.$$

Order.   The order of a determinant of an $n \times n$ matrix is the integer n.

Exercises

1. Write out the determinant of the 4×4 matrix $A = [a_{ij}]$.
2. Find the signs of the following terms in the determinant of the 5×5 matrix $A = [a_{ij}]$.

    a) $a_{51}a_{42}a_{23}a_{35}a_{14}$.

    b) $a_{15}a_{32}a_{43}a_{24}a_{51}$.

    c) $a_{21}a_{13}a_{42}a_{34}a_{55}$.

3. Prove that the product of the elements in the principal diagonal of a matrix is a term in its determinant.
4. Prove that one half the terms in the determinant of a matrix are prefixed by a plus sign and one half by a minus sign.

2 · Cofactors

Note that each term in the determinant $|A|$ contains one and only one element from each row and each column of the matrix A. Thus a term containing a_{11} contains no further elements from the first row or the first column of A. Collect all the terms of $|A|$ containing the element a_{11} as a factor. Then the sum of these terms may be written $a_{11}C_{11}$. The factor C_{11} is called the *cofactor* of a_{11}. Note that the terms in C_{11} are composed of elements taken from the $(n-1) \times (n-1)$ submatrix of A, obtained by deleting the first row and the first column of A. Similarly the sum of all the terms of $|A|$ containing the factor a_{ij} may be written $a_{ij}C_{ij}$, where again the factor C_{ij} is called the cofactor of a_{ij}. The terms of C_{ij} are composed of elements from the submatrix M_{ij} of A, obtained by deleting the ith row and the jth column of A. Thus we may write the determinant $|A|$ as a linear homogeneous function of the elements of the ith row simply by collecting all the terms containing $a_{i1}, a_{i2}, \cdots, a_{in}$, respectively, and forming their sum. Thus

$$|A| = a_{i1}C_{i1} + a_{i2}C_{i2} + \cdots + a_{in}C_{in} = \sum_{j=1}^{n} a_{ij}C_{ij}.$$

Similarly we may write the determinant $|A|$ as a linear homogeneous function of the kth column by collecting all the terms containing $a_{1k}, a_{2k}, \cdots, a_{nk}$, respectively, and forming their sum. Thus

$$|A| = a_{1k}C_{1k} + a_{2k}C_{2k} + \cdots + a_{nk}C_{nk} = \sum_{i=1}^{n} a_{ik}C_{ik}.$$

These two ways of writing the determinant $|A|$ are called the expansions of $|A|$ by the elements and cofactors of the ith row and kth column of $|A|$. We have thus proved the following theorem.

Theorem 1. $|A| = \sum_{j=1}^{n} a_{ij}C_{ij}$ *and* $|A| = \sum_{i=1}^{n} a_{ik}C_{ik}.$

The expansion of a determinant as a linear function of its cofactors enables us to prove the following property of determinants.

Theorem 2. If the elements of the ith row or the kth column of a matrix A are multiplied by an element c of the field, the determinant of the resulting matrix B equals $c|A|$.

Using the first formula in Theorem 1, we have $|B| = \sum_{j=1}^{n} ca_{ij}C_{ij} =$

$c \sum_{j=1}^{n} a_{ij}C_{ij} = c|A|$. To prove the theorem for the kth column we use the second formula. Note that we need not restrict c to being a nonzero constant.

Exercises

1. In the determinant of the 3×3 matrix $A = [a_{ij}]$ exhibit the cofactors $C_{11}, C_{12}, C_{13}.$

2. In the determinant $\begin{vmatrix} 5 & -2 & 1 \\ 3 & 0 & 2 \\ 4 & 1 & 5 \end{vmatrix}$ exhibit the cofactors $C_{11}, C_{12}, C_{13}.$

3. Show that $\begin{vmatrix} 2 & 3 & 4 \\ 5 & 15 & 5 \\ 2 & 9 & 0 \end{vmatrix} = 15 \begin{vmatrix} 2 & 1 & 4 \\ 1 & 1 & 1 \\ 2 & 3 & 0 \end{vmatrix}.$

3 · Further properties

Theorem 3. $|A'| = |A|$, *where* A' *is the transpose of the matrix* A.

Let $A = [a_{ij}]$ be an $n \times n$ matrix. Then $A' = [a_{ji}']$, where $a_{ji}' = a_{ij}$. Apply the definition of a determinant to the matrix A'. The general term of $|A'|$ may be written $t = \text{sgn } p \; a_{j_1 1}' a_{j_2 2}' \cdots a_{j_n n}'$, where $p = \begin{pmatrix} 1 & 2 & \cdots & n \\ j_1 & j_2 & \cdots & j_n \end{pmatrix}$, and where $j_1, j_2, \cdots, j_n$ are $1, 2, \cdots, n$ in some order. Substituting a_{ij} for a_{ji}' in t, we have $t = \text{sgn } p \; a_{1 j_1} a_{2 j_2} \cdots a_{n j_n}$. Except perhaps for sign, this is obviously a term in $|A|$. We determine the permutation p' on the row subscripts of the elements of the principal diagonal of A which would produce this term. Thus the element $a_{1 j_1}$ in t, for example, is obtained from the element $a_{j_1 j_1}$ in the principal diagonal of A by replacing j_1 by 1. Hence $p' = \begin{pmatrix} j_1 & j_2 & \cdots & j_n \\ 1 & 2 & \cdots & n \end{pmatrix} = p^{-1}$. Now $\text{sgn } p = \text{sgn } p^{-1}$, for p^{-1} is an even or an odd permutation according as p is an even or an odd permutation. Thus every term of $|A'|$ is a term of $|A|$, and $|A'| = |A|$.

Theorem 3 thus enables us to replace any theorem concerning the rows of a determinant by a similar theorem concerning its columns, or vice versa.

Theorem 4.   *If in the matrix* A *two rows or two columns are interchanged, the determinant* $|B|$ *of the resulting matrix* B *equals* $-|A|$.

It is convenient to prove the theorem for the interchange of two columns. Then Theorem 3 proves the theorem for the interchange of two rows. Interchange the rth and sth columns of A, where $r < s$, obtaining the matrix B. The product of the elements in the principal diagonal of B is $a_{11} a_{22} \cdots a_{rs} \cdots a_{sr} \cdots a_{nn}$. Then the general term of $|B|$ is $\text{sgn } p \; a_{i_1 1} a_{i_2 2} \cdots a_{i_r s} \cdots a_{i_s r} \cdots a_{i_n n}$, where $p = \begin{pmatrix} 1 & 2 & \cdots & r & \cdots & s & \cdots & n \\ i_1 & i_2 & \cdots & i_r & \cdots & i_s & \cdots & i_n \end{pmatrix}$, and where $i_1, i_2, \cdots, i_n$ are $1, 2, \cdots, n$ in some order. This again, except perhaps for sign, is a term of $|A|$. To obtain this term by a permutation of the row subscripts of the elements in the principal diagonal of A, the permutation $q = \begin{pmatrix} 1 & 2 & \cdots & r & \cdots & s & \cdots & n \\ i_1 & i_2 & \cdots & i_s & \cdots & i_r & \cdots & i_n \end{pmatrix}$ is used. Now

$q = pt$, where $t = (i_r i_s)$. Since t is a transposition, sgn $q = -$sgn p. Moreover, if p runs through the $n!$ permutations of the symmetric group on n symbols, the permutations pt are these same permutations in some order; for recall that, if S is a group and t is an element of the group, $St = S$.

Corollary. If a matrix A *has two identical columns or two identical rows, then* $|A| = 0$.

Interchange the two identical columns of A, obtaining the matrix B. Then $|B| = -|A|$ by the preceding theorem, but $B = A$, and hence $|A| = -|A|$, or $|A| + |A| = 0$. If the elements of A are in a field where $1 + 1 \neq 0$, then $|A| = 0$. The corollary also holds for fields in which $1 + 1 = 0$. For a proof see Exercise 3, p. 130.

Theorem 5. Let C_{ij} *be the cofactor of the element* a_{ij} *in the determinant* $|A| = |a_{ij}|$ *of order* n, *and let* M_{ij} *be the* $(n-1) \times (n-1)$ *submatrix of* A *obtained by deleting the ith row and the jth column of* A. *Then* $C_{ij} = (-1)^{i+j}|M_{ij}|$.

We prove first that $C_{11} = |M_{11}|$. Recall that the terms of $|A|$ which contain a_{11} as a factor are $a_{11}C_{11}$ and that all the elements of the terms of C_{11} are elements of the matrix M_{11}. Thus the general term of $a_{11}C_{11}$ is sgn $p\ a_{11}a_{i_2 2}\, a_{i_3 3} \cdots a_{i_n n}$, where $p = \begin{pmatrix} 1 & 2 & 3 & \cdots & n \\ 1 & i_2 & i_3 & \cdots & i_n \end{pmatrix}$ and $i_2, i_3, \cdots, i_n$ are $2, 3, \cdots, n$ in some order. The permutation p may thus be regarded as a permutation on the symbols $2, 3, \cdots, n$ alone. Hence all the terms of $a_{11}C_{11}$ are obtained by allowing p to run through the $(n-1)!$ permutations on the symbols $2, 3, \cdots, n$, keeping 1 fixed. Thus the terms of C_{11} are obtained by operating on the row subscripts of the elements of the product $a_{22}a_{33} \cdots a_{nn}$ of the elements of the principal diagonal of M_{11}. Therefore $C_{11} = |M_{11}|$.

We now prove that $C_{ij} = (-1)^{i+j}|M_{ij}|$. Move the *i*th row of A into the first row by performing $i - 1$ successive interchanges of adjacent rows of A, and move the *j*th column of A to the first column by performing $j - 1$ successive interchanges of adjacent columns of A. Call the resulting matrix B. The element a_{ij} is thus in the first row and first column of B, and the submatrix of B obtained by deleting its first row and its first column is the submatrix M_{ij} of A. Thus the terms of $|B|$ containing a_{ij} are, according to the first part of our proof, $a_{ij}|M_{ij}|$. But $|B| = (-1)^{i-1+j-1}|A| = (-1)^{i+j}|A|$, and thus $|A| = (-1)^{i+j}|B|$. Now the terms of $|A|$ containing a_{ij} as a factor are $a_{ij}C_{ij}$, and the terms of $|B|$ containing a_{ij} as a factor are $a_{ij}|M_{ij}|$. Therefore $C_{ij} = (-1)^{i+j}|M_{ij}|$.

The determinant $|M_{ij}|$ is called the *minor* of the element a_{ij} in the determinant $|A|$. Note that now Theorem 1 shows how a determinant of order n can be expanded as a linear function of determinants of order $n - 1$.

Theorem 6. The zero formulas. Let C_{ij} *denote the cofactor of the element* a_{ij} *in the determinant* $|A| = |a_{ij}|$ *of order* n. *Then*
$$\sum_{j=1}^{n} a_{ij}C_{kj} = 0 \text{ and } \sum_{j=1}^{n} a_{ji}C_{jk} = 0, \text{ if } i \neq k.$$

The first formula becomes self-evident when we recall that the cofactors C_{kj}, with $j = 1, 2, \cdots, n$, are determinants of order $n - 1$ formed from the elements of $|A|$ that lie in all the rows of A except the kth row. Thus, if in the sum $\sum_{j=1}^{n} a_{kj}C_{kj}$ we replace the elements a_{kj} of the kth row of A by the elements a_{ij} of the ith row of A, when $i \neq k$, we obtain the desired sum. We now see, however, that this sum is the determinant of the matrix B obtained from A by replacing the kth row of A by its ith row. Thus the matrix B has two rows alike, and hence $|B| = 0$. Similarly the sum $\sum_{j=1}^{n} a_{ji}C_{jk}$, when $i \neq k$, represents the determinant of the matrix C obtained from A by replacing the kth column of A by its ith column. Since C has two columns alike, $|C| = 0$.

Theorem 7. If in the n $\times$ n *matrix* A $= [a_{ij}]$ *the* kth *row* A_k *of* A *is replaced by the row* $A_k + cA_i$, *with* i $\neq$ k, *the determinant of the resulting matrix equals the determinant of* A.

Let B be the matrix obtained from A by replacing the kth row of A by $A_k + cA_i$, with $i \neq k$. Expand the determinant $|B|$ by the elements and the cofactors of its kth row. Thus

$$|B| = \sum_{j=1}^{n} (a_{kj} + ca_{ij})C_{kj} = \sum_{j=1}^{n} a_{kj}C_{kj} + c\sum_{j=1}^{n} a_{ij}C_{kj}$$
$$= |A| + 0 = |A|$$

by Theorem 1 and Theorem 6. A similar theorem obviously also holds for the columns of a determinant.

The above theorems are used to simplify the labor of computing the value of a determinant. If, for example, in a determinant of order n all the elements except one in a row or column are made zero, the determinant can be written as the product of this non-zero element times its cofactor, a determinant of order $n - 1$. Applying this rule successively to the determinant of a diagonal matrix, i.e., a matrix in which all the terms are zero except those in the principal diagonal, we see that the determinant of a diagonal matrix is the product of the elements in the principal diagonal.

Example. We use the above theorems to evaluate Vandermonde's determinant of order 3.

$$|A| = \begin{vmatrix} 1 & 1 & 1 \\ x & y & z \\ x^2 & y^2 & z^2 \end{vmatrix} = \begin{vmatrix} 1 & 0 & 0 \\ x & y - x & z - x \\ x^2 & y^2 - x^2 & z^2 - x^2 \end{vmatrix}$$

$$= (y - x)(z - x) \begin{vmatrix} 1 & 0 & 0 \\ x & 1 & 1 \\ x^2 & y + x & z + x \end{vmatrix}$$

$$= (y - x)(z - x) \begin{vmatrix} 1 & 1 \\ y + x & z + x \end{vmatrix}$$

$$= (y - x)(z - x)(z - y).$$

However, we can evaluate this determinant more simply by noting that, if it is expanded in terms of the elements and cofactors of the first column, we may regard it as a polynomial in x. Thus, if $x = y$, we see that the determinant is zero, for it has two columns alike. Hence $x - y$ is a factor of the determinant. Similarly $x - z$ is a factor, and regarding the determinant as a polynomial in y, we see that $y - z$ is a factor. Thus $|A| = (x - y)(x - z)(y - z)b$, where b is to be determined. Since the product of the elements in the principal diagonal is a term in $|A|$, yz^2 is a term in $|A|$. The coefficient of yz^2 in our expansion is $-b$. Hence $b = -1$. Similarly, we can prove that Vandermonde's determinant of order n has the following factorization:

$$\begin{vmatrix} 1 & 1 & 1 & \cdots & 1 \\ x_1 & x_2 & x_3 & \cdots & x_n \\ x_1^2 & x_2^2 & x_3^2 & \cdots & x_n^2 \\ \cdots\cdots\cdots\cdots\cdots\cdots\cdots \\ x_1^{n-1} & x_2^{n-1} & x_3^{n-1} & \cdots & x_n^{n-1} \end{vmatrix} = \prod_{i>j}^{n} (x_i - x_j).$$

Exercises

1. Find the values of $\begin{vmatrix} 3 & 4 & -2 & 1 \\ 2 & 4 & 6 & 8 \\ 1 & 8 & 3 & 2 \\ 0 & 0 & 2 & 0 \end{vmatrix}$ and $\begin{vmatrix} 5 & 2 & -1 & 3 \\ 1 & 2 & 1 & 1 \\ -1 & 3 & 0 & 0 \\ 3 & 0 & 0 & 1 \end{vmatrix}$.

2. Let $|A| = |a_{ij}|$ be of order 4, and let C_{ij} be the cofactor of the element a_{ij}. Exhibit a matrix whose determinant equals $\sum_{j=1}^{4} x_j C_{3j}$. Exhibit a matrix whose determinant equals $\sum_{j=1}^{4} x_j C_{j2}$.

3. Prove by induction that the determinant of a matrix with two rows alike is zero. Hint: Check that this is true for a determinant of order 2. Use the cofactor expansion of a determinant.

4. Without expanding prove that the skew-symmetric determinant of odd order n over a field whose characteristic is not 2 equals zero; i.e., $|a_{ij}| = 0$, if $a_{ii} = 0$ and $a_{ij} = -a_{ji}$.

5. Prove that $\begin{vmatrix} a_1 + b_1 & c_1 & d_1 \\ a_2 + b_2 & c_2 & d_2 \\ a_3 + b_3 & c_3 & d_3 \end{vmatrix} = \begin{vmatrix} a_1 & c_1 & d_1 \\ a_2 & c_2 & d_2 \\ a_3 & c_3 & d_3 \end{vmatrix} + \begin{vmatrix} b_1 & c_1 & d_1 \\ b_2 & c_2 & d_2 \\ b_3 & c_3 & d_3 \end{vmatrix}$.

6. Write the following determinants as products of factors:

a) $\begin{vmatrix} 1 & x & 1 & y \\ x & 1 & y & 1 \\ 1 & y & 1 & x \\ y & 1 & x & 1 \end{vmatrix}$.   b) $\begin{vmatrix} b+c & a & a \\ b & c+a & b \\ c & c & a+b \end{vmatrix}$.

c) $\begin{vmatrix} x & a & b & c & 1 \\ d & x & e & f & 1 \\ d & g & x & h & 1 \\ d & g & k & x & 1 \\ d & g & k & m & 1 \end{vmatrix}$.   d) $\begin{vmatrix} a & x & y & a \\ x & 0 & 0 & y \\ y & 0 & 0 & x \\ a & y & x & a \end{vmatrix}$.

e) $\begin{vmatrix} a & b & b & b \\ a & b & a & a \\ a & a & b & a \\ b & b & b & a \end{vmatrix}$.

7. Let $A = [a_{ij}]$ be an $n \times n$ matrix, with $a_{ij} = 1$ when $i \neq j$, and $a_{ii} = 0$. Prove that $|A| = (n - 1)(-1)^{n-1}$.

4 · Laplace's expansion of a determinant

Definition. Let D be an $r \times r$ submatrix of an $n \times n$ matrix A. The determinant of the submatrix D' of A obtained by deleting the r rows and r columns of A in which the elements of D lie is called the *complementary minor* of the minor $|D|$.

Theorem 8. The determinant of the $n \times n$ matrix $A = [a_{ij}]$ equals the sum of the signed products $\pm |D_i| \cdot |D_i'|$, where $|D_i|$ is an $r \times r$ minor of A formed from the elements of the first r columns of A and where $|D_i'|$ is its complementary minor. The plus sign or the minus sign is prefixed according as an even number or an odd number of interchanges of adjacent rows of A is necessary to bring the submatrix D_i into the first r rows of A.

This is called Laplace's expansion by the minors of the first r columns. The proof will make it obvious that any r columns or any r rows of A can be used if proper account is taken of the signs of the products.

Example. Let $|A| = \begin{vmatrix} a_1 & a_2 & a_3 & a_4 \\ b_1 & b_2 & b_3 & b_4 \\ c_1 & c_2 & c_3 & c_4 \\ d_1 & d_2 & d_3 & d_4 \end{vmatrix}$. Expand by the minors of the first two columns.   Thus

$$|A| = \begin{vmatrix} a_1 & a_2 \\ b_1 & b_2 \end{vmatrix} \cdot \begin{vmatrix} c_3 & c_4 \\ d_3 & d_4 \end{vmatrix} - \begin{vmatrix} a_1 & a_2 \\ c_1 & c_2 \end{vmatrix} \cdot \begin{vmatrix} b_3 & b_4 \\ d_3 & d_4 \end{vmatrix}$$

$$+ \begin{vmatrix} a_1 & a_2 \\ d_1 & d_2 \end{vmatrix} \cdot \begin{vmatrix} b_3 & b_4 \\ c_3 & c_4 \end{vmatrix} + \begin{vmatrix} b_1 & b_2 \\ c_1 & c_2 \end{vmatrix} \cdot \begin{vmatrix} a_3 & a_4 \\ d_3 & d_4 \end{vmatrix}$$

$$- \begin{vmatrix} b_1 & b_2 \\ d_1 & d_2 \end{vmatrix} \cdot \begin{vmatrix} a_3 & a_4 \\ c_3 & c_4 \end{vmatrix} + \begin{vmatrix} c_1 & c_2 \\ d_1 & d_2 \end{vmatrix} \cdot \begin{vmatrix} a_3 & a_4 \\ b_3 & b_4 \end{vmatrix}.$$

Proof.   Let

$$|D_1| = \begin{vmatrix} a_{11} & \cdots & a_{1r} \\ \cdots & \cdots & \cdots \\ a_{r1} & \cdots & a_{rr} \end{vmatrix} \text{ and } |D_1'| = \begin{vmatrix} a_{r+1,r+1} & \cdots & a_{r+1,n} \\ \cdots & \cdots & \cdots \\ a_{n,r+1} & \cdots & a_{nn} \end{vmatrix}.$$

Apply the definition of a determinant to $|D_1|$ and to $|D_1'|$.   The general term in $|D_1|$ is sgn $p\ a_{i_1 1} a_{i_2 2} \cdots a_{i_r r}$, where

$$p = \begin{pmatrix} 1 & 2 & \cdots & r \\ i_1 & i_2 & \cdots & i_r \end{pmatrix}$$

and where $i_1, i_2, \cdots, i_r$ are $1, 2, \cdots, r$ in some order.   The general term in $|D_1'|$ is sgn $q\ a_{i_{r+1}r+1} \cdots a_{i_n n}$, where

$$q = \begin{pmatrix} r+1 & \cdots & n \\ i_{r+1} & \cdots & i_n \end{pmatrix},$$

and where $i_{r+1}, \cdots, i_n$ are $r+1, \cdots, n$ in some order.   Clearly the general term in the product $|D_1| \cdot |D_1'|$ is (sgn p)(sgn q) $a_{i_1 1}$ $\cdots a_{i_r r} a_{i_{r+1}r+1} \cdots a_{i_n n}$.   This is a term in $|A|$, for it can be obtained from the principal diagonal of A by the permutation pq. Thus every term in $|D_1| \cdot |D_1'|$ is a term of $|A|$.   Now consider the product $|D_i| \cdot |D_i'|$, with $i > 1$.   Interchange adjacent rows of A so that the submatrix D_i occurs in the first r rows of the re-sulting matrix B.   As in the first case discussed, the terms of $|D_i| \cdot |D_i'|$ are terms of $|B|$.   If B has been obtained from A by making k interchanges of adjacent rows, then $|B| = (-1)^k |A|$, and hence the terms of $(-1)^k |D_i| \cdot |D_i'|$ are terms of $|A|$.   Clearly the terms of $|D_i| \cdot |D_i'|$ and $|D_j| \cdot |D_j'|$, with $j \neq i$, are distinct. There are $C(n, r) = n!/[r!(n - r)!]$ products $|D_i| \cdot |D_i'|$, and each product contains $r!(n - r)!$ terms. Thus the sum of these signed products contains $C(n, r)r!(n - r)! = n!$ terms. Laplace's expansion has therefore been verified.

Exercises

1. Expand by Laplace's development by the minors of the first two columns and simplify the resulting sum:

$$\begin{vmatrix} a & 1 & 0 & 0 & 0 \\ b & a & 1 & 0 & 0 \\ 0 & b & a & 1 & 0 \\ 0 & 0 & b & a & 1 \\ 0 & 0 & 0 & b & a \end{vmatrix}.$$

2. Express as the product of two determinants of order 2:

$$\begin{vmatrix} 0 & 1 & x & y \\ 1 & 0 & y & x \\ z & w & 0 & 0 \\ w & z & 0 & 0 \end{vmatrix}.$$

5 · Products of determinants

We shall now develop some properties of the product of determinants. The determinant of the $n \times n$ identity matrix I is 1. Let E be a matrix obtained from the identity matrix by performing one elementary row operation. It is obvious from the properties of determinants that $|E| = -1$, c, or 1 according as the first, second, or third elementary row operation has been performed on I. Now let A be an $n \times n$ matrix. Then $|EA| = -|A|$, $c|A|$, or $|A|$, and $|EA| = |AE|$. Hence we have proved the following theorem.

Theorem 9. *If* E *is an elementary matrix,* $|EA| = |AE| = |E| \cdot |A| = |A| \cdot |E|$.

We use this theorem to prove

Theorem 10. *An* n $\times$ n *matrix* A *is nonsingular if and only if* $|A| \neq 0$.

Let C be the canonical form of the matrix A. Then there exist nonsingular matrices S and T such that $SAT = C$. Hence $A =$

$S^{-1}CT^{-1} = E_1E_2 \cdots E_s \ C \ E_1'E_2' \cdots E_t'$, where the E_i and the E_i' are elementary matrices. Now, making successive applications of Theorem 9, we have $|A| = |E_1E_2 \cdots E_s \ C \ E_1'E_2' \cdots E_t'| = |E_1| \cdot |E_2| \cdots |E_s| \cdot |C| \cdot |E_1'| \cdot |E_2'| \cdots |E_t'|$. Since the determinants of the elementary matrices are not zero, we see that $|A| = 0$ if and only if $|C| = 0$. But $|C| = 0$ if and only if it has a row of zeros, i.e., if and only if A is of rank $< n$. Thus A is nonsingular if and only if $|A| \neq 0$.

The following theorem gives us a rule for multiplying together two determinants of order n to obtain a determinant of order n. We merely multiply together the matrices of the two determinants and find the determinant of the resulting matrix.

Theorem 11. $|AB| = |A| \cdot |B|$.

Let C_a and C_b be the canonical forms of the matrices A and B respectively. Then $A = D_1D_2 \cdots D_rC_aE_1E_2 \cdots E_s$ and $B = F_1F_2 \cdots F_tC_bG_1G_2 \cdots G_u$, where the D_i, E_i, F_i, and G_i are elementary matrices. Thus

$$AB = D_1D_2 \cdots D_rC_aE_1E_2 \cdots E_sF_1F_2 \cdots F_tC_bG_1G_2 \cdots G_u,$$

and, using Theorem 9, we have

$$|AB| = |D_1D_2 \cdots D_r| \cdot |C_aE_1E_2 \cdots E_sF_1F_2 \cdots F_tC_b| \cdot |G_1G_2 \cdots G_u|.$$

Now if A and B are nonsingular, C_a and C_b are identity matrices, and, using Theorem 9 again, we have

$$|AB| = |D_1D_2 \cdots D_rC_aE_1E_2 \cdots E_s| \cdot |F_1F_2 \cdots F_tC_bG_1G_2 \cdots G_u|$$
$$= |A| \cdot |B|.$$

If A is singular, C_a has a row of zeros, and hence $M = C_aE_1E_2 \cdots E_sF_1F_2 \cdots F_sC_b$ has a row of zeros. Thus $|M| = 0$ and $|AB| = 0$. If B is singular, C_b has a column of zeros, and hence M has a column of zeros, giving us again $|M| = 0$ and $|AB| = 0$. Now if either A or B is singular, $|A| \cdot |B| = 0$, and hence $|AB| = |A| \cdot |B|$.

Theorem 12. $|AB'| = |A| \cdot |B|$, *where* B' *is the transpose of the matrix* B.

Note that this theorem indicates a second way to multiply two determinants of order n: we merely find the determinant of the matrix AB'. To state the result loosely, this theorem gives us a row-by-row rule for the multiplication of two determinants. The proof consists in observing that $|AB'| = |A| \cdot |B'| = |A| \cdot |B|$, for the determinant of the transpose of a matrix equals the determinant of the matrix.

Example.
$$\begin{vmatrix} 1 & 2 \\ -1 & 3 \end{vmatrix} \cdot \begin{vmatrix} 0 & -1 \\ 2 & 1 \end{vmatrix} = \begin{vmatrix} 4 & 1 \\ 6 & 4 \end{vmatrix}$$
if the multiplication has been performed by using the row-times-column rule, but

the product $= \begin{vmatrix} -2 & 4 \\ -3 & 1 \end{vmatrix}$ if the multiplication has been performed by using the row-by-row rule.

6 · Adjoint and inverse of a matrix

Definition. Let $A = [a_{ij}]$ be an $n \times n$ matrix. Let C_{ij} be the cofactor of the element a_{ij}. Then the matrix $[C_{ji}']$, where the element C_{ji}' in the jth row and the ith column equals C_{ij}, is called the adjoint of A, often written adj A.

Theorem 13. $\mathrm{A}(adj\ \mathrm{A}) = |\mathrm{A}|\mathrm{I}$, *and* $(adj\ \mathrm{A})\mathrm{A} = |\mathrm{A}|\mathrm{I}$.

The element in the kth row and ith column of the product $A[C_{ji}']$ is $\sum_{j=1}^{n} a_{kj}C_{ji}' = \sum_{j=1}^{n} a_{kj}C_{ij}$, which by Theorem 6 equals zero if $k \neq i$, and which by Theorem 1 equals $|A|$ if $k = i$. Hence A (adj A) is a diagonal matrix with diagonal elements equal to $|A|$. Thus A (adj A) $= |A|I$. Similarly the element in the jth row and the kth column of the product $[C_{ji}']A$ is $\sum_{i=1}^{n} C_{ji}'a_{ik} = \sum_{i=1}^{n} C_{ij}a_{ik}$, which equals zero if $j \neq k$, and which equals $|A|$ if $j = k$.

Hence from the definition of the inverse of a matrix, we have the following corollary.

Corollary. $\mathrm{A}^{-1} = (adj\ \mathrm{A})/|\mathrm{A}|$.

Example. The adjoint of the matrix $A = \begin{bmatrix} 2 & -1 & 3 \\ 0 & 2 & 0 \\ 2 & 1 & 1 \end{bmatrix}$ is

$$\begin{bmatrix} \begin{vmatrix} 2 & 0 \\ 1 & 1 \end{vmatrix} & -\begin{vmatrix} -1 & 3 \\ 1 & 1 \end{vmatrix} & \begin{vmatrix} -1 & 3 \\ 2 & 0 \end{vmatrix} \\ -\begin{vmatrix} 0 & 0 \\ 2 & 1 \end{vmatrix} & \begin{vmatrix} 2 & 3 \\ 2 & 1 \end{vmatrix} & -\begin{vmatrix} 2 & 3 \\ 0 & 0 \end{vmatrix} \\ \begin{vmatrix} 0 & 2 \\ 2 & 1 \end{vmatrix} & -\begin{vmatrix} 2 & -1 \\ 2 & 1 \end{vmatrix} & \begin{vmatrix} 2 & -1 \\ 0 & 2 \end{vmatrix} \end{bmatrix} = \begin{bmatrix} 2 & 4 & -6 \\ 0 & -4 & 0 \\ -4 & -4 & 4 \end{bmatrix}$$

and $A(\text{adj } A) = \begin{bmatrix} -8 & 0 & 0 \\ 0 & -8 & 0 \\ 0 & 0 & -8 \end{bmatrix} = -8\begin{bmatrix} 1 & 0 & 0 \\ 0 & 1 & 0 \\ 0 & 0 & 1 \end{bmatrix}.$ The in-

verse of A is $\begin{bmatrix} -\frac{1}{4} & -\frac{1}{2} & \frac{3}{4} \\ 0 & \frac{1}{2} & 0 \\ \frac{1}{2} & \frac{1}{2} & -\frac{1}{2} \end{bmatrix}.$

Exercises

1. Perform the multiplication of the two determinants in two ways and exhibit the resulting determinants:

a) $\begin{vmatrix} 1 & -1 & 2 \\ 3 & 4 & 1 \\ 0 & 2 & 2 \end{vmatrix} \cdot \begin{vmatrix} 0 & 2 & 1 \\ 0 & 1 & 1 \\ 2 & -1 & 1 \end{vmatrix}.$

b) $\begin{vmatrix} a & 0 & a \\ b & 0 & b \\ c & c & c \end{vmatrix} \cdot \begin{vmatrix} 1 & 1 & -1 \\ 2 & 0 & 2 \\ 1 & 1 & 1 \end{vmatrix}.$

2. Find the adjoints and the inverses of the following matrices:

a) $\begin{bmatrix} 1 & 2 & 3 \\ 0 & 5 & 0 \\ 2 & 4 & 3 \end{bmatrix}.$ b) $\begin{bmatrix} 3 & -1 & 2 \\ 1 & 0 & 3 \\ 4 & 0 & 2 \end{bmatrix}.$ c) $\begin{bmatrix} 2 & 3 & -1 \\ 0 & 1 & -1 \\ 2 & 1 & 2 \end{bmatrix}.$

3. Find the product $A(\text{adj } A)$ if $A = \begin{bmatrix} 3 & 2 & -1 \\ 1 & -3 & 2 \\ 5 & -4 & 3 \end{bmatrix}.$

7 · Cramer's rule

The last corollary proves *Cramer's rule* for solving n simultaneous linear equations in n unknowns.

Theorem 14. If the n *simultaneous linear equations in* n *unknowns* $\sum_{j=1}^{n} a_{ij}x_j = c_i$, *with* $i = 1, 2, \cdots, n$, *have a nonzero determinant of coefficients* $|A| = |a_{ij}|$, *then the equations have the unique solutions* $x_j = \dfrac{C_{1j}c_1 + C_{2j}c_2 + \cdots + C_{nj}c_n}{|A|}$, *with* $j = 1, 2, \cdots, n$, *where* C_{ij} *is the cofactor of the element* a_{ij} *in* $|A|$.

Letting $X = \begin{bmatrix} x_1 \\ x_2 \\ \cdot \\ \cdot \\ \cdot \\ x_n \end{bmatrix}$ and $C = \begin{bmatrix} c_1 \\ c_2 \\ \cdot \\ \cdot \\ \cdot \\ c_n \end{bmatrix}$, write the equations in matrix

form $AX = C$. Then the solution is, as we have seen, $X = A^{-1}C$. The form of the solution in the theorem is found by using $A^{-1} = (\text{adj } A)/|A|$. Thus the element in the jth row of the matrix solution is

$$x_j = \sum_{i=1}^{n} \frac{C_{ji}{}' c_i}{|A|} = \sum_{i=1}^{n} \frac{C_{ij}c_i}{|A|}.$$

Note that the numerator in the solution is

$$\begin{vmatrix} a_{11} & \cdots & a_{1,j-1} & c_1 & a_{1,j+1} & \cdots & a_{1n} \\ a_{21} & \cdots & a_{2,j-1} & c_2 & a_{2,j+1} & \cdots & a_{2n} \\ \cdots\cdots & & \cdots\cdots & \cdots & \cdots\cdots & & \cdots\cdots \\ a_{n1} & \cdots & a_{n,j-1} & c_n & a_{n,j+1} & \cdots & a_{nn} \end{vmatrix},$$

which is the determinant obtained by replacing the jth column of $|A|$ by the constants c_i, $i = 1, 2, \cdots, n$.

Exercises

Use Cramer's rule in finding the solutions of the following equations:

1. $2x + 3y - 4z = -8$,
   $3x + 2y + 4z = 3$,
   $5x - 4y + 5z = 18$.

2. $3x + y + z + w = 0$,
   $2x - y + 2z - w = 4$,
   $x + 2z + w = 3$,
   $2x + 3z + w = 1$.

8 · Determinant rank of a matrix

Definition.   An $m \times n$ matrix A is said to be of determinant rank d, if there exists a $d \times d$ submatrix D of A whose determinant $|D| \neq 0$, and if the determinant of every $(d + 1) \times (d + 1)$ submatrix of A is zero.

Note that this definition implies that the determinant of any $r \times r$ submatrix of A, with $r > d + 1$, is zero, for a determinant is a linear homogeneous function of the cofactors of a row or a column, and the cofactors are determinants of order $r - 1$ if the determinant is of order r.   Thus any determinant of order $r > d + 1$ can finally be expressed as a linear sum of determinants of order $d + 1$ and hence must be zero.

Theorem 15.   *The rank of a matrix equals its determinant rank.*

Let d be the determinant rank of a matrix A, and let r be its rank.   Thus A has a $d \times d$ submatrix D whose determinant $|D| \neq 0$.   Consider those rows of A in which D lies.   The rows of D are linearly independent since D is nonsingular.   Hence the d rows of A which contribute elements to the rows of D are linearly independent, for a linear relation between the rows of A is also a linear relation between the rows of D.   Hence the maximum number r of linearly independent rows of A is at least d; i.e., $r \geq d$. We shall now prove that $r \leq d$.   Consider r rows of A which are linearly independent, and denote by R the $r \times n$ submatrix of A formed by these r rows.   Now since the row rank of R is r, its column rank is also r.   Hence R has r linearly independent columns.   Let R_1 be the $r \times r$ submatrix of R formed by these linearly independent columns.   It is nonsingular, and hence $|R_1| \neq 0$.   But R_1 is also a submatrix of A.   Hence $r \leq d$.   Recalling the previous inequality $r \geq d$, we conclude that $r = d$.

Note that we have incidentally proved the following useful corollary.

Corollary.   *Any* d *rows of a matrix which contain a* d $\times$ d *submatrix whose determinant is not zero are linearly independent.*

Exercises

Determine whether the rows of each of the following matrices are linearly dependent.   If they are linearly dependent, find a maximum subset that is linearly independent.

1. $\begin{bmatrix} 1 & 0 & 1 & 1 \\ 1 & -1 & 1 & -1 \\ 2 & 1 & 0 & 2 \\ 4 & -1 & 2 & -4 \end{bmatrix}.$ 2. $\begin{bmatrix} 3 & 4 & -1 & 1 \\ 1 & 1 & 1 & -1 \\ 2 & 3 & -2 & 2 \\ 5 & 7 & -3 & 3 \end{bmatrix}.$

3. $\begin{bmatrix} 2 & 3 & -4 & 5 \\ 1 & -1 & 2 & -1 \\ 4 & 1 & 0 & 3 \\ 7 & 3 & -2 & 7 \end{bmatrix}.$

9 · Polynomials with matrix coefficients

Let A_i denote $n \times n$ matrices over a field F. Form the polynomial

$$f(x) = A_0 + A_1 x + A_2 x^2 + \cdots + A_n x^n$$

in the indeterminate x. The symbol x acts as a scalar with respect to the matrix coefficients. Thus $f(x)$ may also be regarded as a matrix. For example, we may write

$$f(x) = \begin{bmatrix} 1 & 0 \\ 2 & -1 \end{bmatrix} + \begin{bmatrix} 1 & -1 \\ 0 & 0 \end{bmatrix} x + \begin{bmatrix} 3 & 1 \\ 0 & 1 \end{bmatrix} x^2$$

$$= \begin{bmatrix} 1 + x + 3x^2 & -x + x^2 \\ 2 & -1 + x^2 \end{bmatrix}.$$

If $g(x) = B_0 + B_1 x + \cdots + B_m x^m$, where the B_i are $n \times n$ matrices over the field F, we can define the sum and product of $f(x)$ and $g(x)$ as usual:

$$f(x) + g(x) = (A_0 + B_0) + (A_1 + B_1)x + \cdots$$
$$+ (A_m + B_m)x^m + A_{m+1}x^{m+1} + \cdots + A_n x^n, \qquad n > m,$$

$$h(x) = f(x) \cdot g(x) = A_0 B_0 + (A_0 B_1 + A_1 B_0)x + \cdots$$
$$+ (A_0 B_k + A_1 B_{k-1} + \cdots + A_k B_0)x^k + \cdots + A_n B_m x^{n+m}.$$

We are interested in defining a functional value of $f(x)$ when we substitute a matrix C for x. Since the multiplication of matrices is not commutative, the necessity for a definition is obvious, for we now see that x is replaced by a symbol that is no longer commutative with each matrix. For example, if

$$f(x) = \begin{bmatrix} 1 & 0 \\ -1 & 2 \end{bmatrix} + \begin{bmatrix} 2 & -1 \\ 3 & 2 \end{bmatrix} x = \begin{bmatrix} 1 & 0 \\ -1 & 2 \end{bmatrix} + x \begin{bmatrix} 2 & -1 \\ 3 & 2 \end{bmatrix},$$

and if we wish to substitute $\begin{bmatrix} 1 & 1 \\ 1 & -1 \end{bmatrix}$ for x, we note that the

matrix $\begin{bmatrix} 1 & 0 \\ -1 & 2 \end{bmatrix} + \begin{bmatrix} 2 & -1 \\ 3 & 2 \end{bmatrix} \begin{bmatrix} 1 & 1 \\ 1 & -1 \end{bmatrix} \neq \begin{bmatrix} 1 & 0 \\ -1 & 2 \end{bmatrix}$

$$+ \begin{bmatrix} 1 & 1 \\ 1 & -1 \end{bmatrix} \begin{bmatrix} 2 & -1 \\ 3 & 2 \end{bmatrix}.$$

Hence we define a right functional value $f_R(C)$ and a left functional value $f_L(C)$ as follows:

$$f_R(C) = A_0 + A_1 C + A_2 C^2 + \cdots + A_n C^n$$

and

$$f_L(C) = A_0 + C A_1 + C^2 A_2 + \cdots + C^n A_n.$$

It is easy to see that, if $f(x) \cdot g(x) = h(x)$, then $f_R(C) \cdot g_R(C) \neq h_R(C)$. However, we can prove the following theorem.

Theorem 16. Let $\mathrm{f}(\mathrm{x}) \cdot \mathrm{g}(\mathrm{x}) = \mathrm{h}(\mathrm{x})$, *where* $\mathrm{f}(\mathrm{x})$, $\mathrm{g}(\mathrm{x})$, *and* $\mathrm{h}(\mathrm{x})$ *are polynomials whose coefficients are matrices over a field. Let* C *be a matrix such that* $\mathrm{g}_R(\mathrm{C}) = 0$. *Then* $\mathrm{h}_R(\mathrm{C}) = 0$.

Using the notation for $f(x)$, $g(x)$, and $h(x)$ given above, we have

$$\begin{aligned} h_R(C) &= A_0 B_0 + (A_0 B_1 + A_1 B_0)C + (A_0 B_2 + A_1 B_1 + A_2 B_0)C^2 \\ &\quad + \cdots + A_n B_m C^{n+m} \\ &= A_0(B_0 + B_1 C + B_2 C^2 + \cdots + B_m C^m) \\ &\quad + A_1(B_0 + B_1 C + \cdots + B_m C^m)C + \cdots \\ &\quad + A_k(B_0 + B_1 C + \cdots + B_m C^m)C^k + \cdots \\ &\quad + A_n(B_0 + B_1 C + \cdots + B_m C^m)C^n \\ &= A_0 g_R(C) + A_1 g_R(C)C + \cdots + A_n g_R(C)C^n. \end{aligned}$$

Thus, if $g_R(C) = 0$, $h_R(C) = 0$. Similarly it can be proved that, if $f_L(C) = 0$, then $h_L(C) = 0$.

From this theorem we observe that the theory of polynomials

with matrix coefficients is more complicated than the theory of polynomials over a field.

Characteristic polynomial of a matrix. Let A be an $n \times n$ matrix over a field F. Form the matrix $A - xI$, where I is the $n \times n$ identity matrix and x is an indeterminate. The determinant $|A - xI| = b_0 + b_1x + \cdots + (-1)^n x^n = f(x)$ is called the characteristic polynomial of the matrix A.

Example. Let $A = \begin{bmatrix} 2 & -1 \\ -6 & 1 \end{bmatrix}$. Then

$$A - xI = \begin{bmatrix} 2 - x & -1 \\ -6 & 1 - x \end{bmatrix}$$

and $|A - xI| = -4 - 3x + x^2 = f(x)$. A simple computation shows that $-4I - 3A + A^2$ is the zero matrix. We shall now prove in general that, if a matrix A is substituted for x in its characteristic polynomial, and if the constant term in the polynomial is multiplied by the identity matrix, the resulting sum is the zero matrix. Thus a matrix A is said to be a zero of its characteristic polynomial.

Theorem 17. Cayley-Hamilton theorem. Let A *be an* $n \times n$ *matrix over a field and let* $f(x) = b_0 + b_1x + b_2x^2 + \cdots + (-1)^n x^n$ *be its characteristic polynomial. Then* $b_0 I + b_1 A + b_2 A^2 + \cdots + (-1)^n A^n = 0$.

Now $\operatorname{adj}(A - xI) \cdot (A - xI) = f(x)I$. The elements of $\operatorname{adj}(A - xI)$ are polynomials in x of degree at most $n - 1$ with coefficients in the field F. Hence $\operatorname{adj}(A - xI)$ may be regarded as a polynomial in x of degree at most $n - 1$ with matrix coefficients over F. Thus $\operatorname{adj}(A - xI) \cdot (A - xI)$ is the product of two polynomials with matrix coefficients which equals a polynomial in x of degree n whose coefficients are scalar matrices over F. Note that $A - AI = 0$. Hence by the previous theorem $f_R(A)I = 0$, but since the coefficients of $f(x)I$ are scalar matrices the right and left functional values are the same. Hence we may write $f(A)I = 0$, which is the desired result.

Definition. The zeros of the characteristic polynomial of a matrix over a field F are called the characteristic roots of the matrix. If the field F is the field of complex numbers, then the characteristic polynomial of an $n \times n$ matrix over F always has n zeros that are complex numbers.

10 · Similar matrices over a field

Definition. If a nonsingular matrix S exists such that $S^{-1}AS = B$, then A and B are said to be similar.

Note that similarity of matrices is a special case of the equivalence of matrices. We shall give some of the simpler properties of similar matrices.

Theorem 18. The determinants of similar matrices are equal.

Let $B = S^{-1}AS$. Then $|B| = |S^{-1}AS| = |S^{-1}| \cdot |A| \cdot |S| = |A| \cdot |S^{-1}| \cdot |S| = |A| \cdot |S^{-1}S| = |A| \cdot |I| = |A|$.

Theorem 19. Similar matrices have the same characteristic polynomial.

Let $B = S^{-1}AS$. Then

$$B - xI = S^{-1}AS - xI = S^{-1}AS - S^{-1}(xI)S$$
$$= S^{-1}(AS - xIS) = S^{-1}(A - xI)S.$$

Hence

$$|B - xI| = |S^{-1}| \cdot |A - xI| \cdot |S| = |A - xI|.$$

Diagonal matrices have particularly simple properties. For example, their determinants are the products of the elements in their principal diagonals, and the product of two diagonal matrices is a diagonal matrix. Moreover, the characteristic polynomial of a diagonal matrix whose diagonal elements are $d_1, d_2, \cdots, d_n$ is $(d_1 - x)(d_2 - x) \cdots (d_n - x)$, and hence its characteristic roots are $d_1, d_2, \cdots, d_n$. It is of interest to examine one simple example of a matrix that is similar to a diagonal matrix.

Theorem 20. Let A be an $n \times n$ matrix over the field of complex numbers. If the characteristic roots of the matrix A are distinct, then A is similar to a diagonal matrix.

Let $|A - xI| = f(x)$ have the distinct zeros $r_1, r_2, \cdots, r_n$. We construct a nonsingular matrix S such that $S^{-1}AS$ is a diagonal matrix with diagonal elements $r_1, r_2, \cdots, r_n$. We first show that we can find nonzero $n \times 1$ matrices, or vectors, S_j, such that $AS_j = r_jS_j$. Denote the elements of S_j by $s_{1j}, s_{2j}, \cdots, s_{nj}$.

Now $AS_j = r_jS_j$ may be written $(A - r_jI)S_j = 0$, which is a system of n linear homogeneous equations in the n unknowns s_{ij}, with $i = 1, 2, \cdots, n$. This system has a solution other than $(0, 0, \cdots, 0)$ if and only if the determinant $|A - r_jI| = 0$. But r_j is a zero of $f(x)$, and hence we have the desired nonzero solutions for each j. The columns of the matrix S are the n columns S_j.

We show next that the n columns S_j are linearly independent. Suppose that a linear relation $\sum_{j=1}^{n} c_jS_j = 0$ exists. The method we use to show that $c_1 = 0$, for example, will prove that each $c_j = 0$, for $j = 1, 2, \cdots, n$. Multiply the matrix equation $\sum_{j=1}^{n} c_jS_j = 0$ on the left by the product

$$(A - r_2I)(A - r_3I) \cdots (A - r_nI),$$

obtaining

$$(A - r_2I)(A - r_3I)$$
$$\cdots (A - r_nI)(c_1S_1 + c_2S_2 + \cdots + c_nS_n) = 0.$$

Note that the factors $(A - r_jI)$ are commutative with each other. Now, for $k \neq j$,

$$(A - r_jI)c_kS_k = (AS_k - r_jS_k)c_k = (r_kS_k - r_jS_k)c_k$$
$$= (r_k - r_j)S_kc_k,$$

but, for $k = j$,

$$(A - r_jI)c_jS_j = (r_jS_j - r_jS_j)c_j = 0.$$

Thus

$$(A - r_2I)(A - r_3I) \cdots (A - r_nI)(c_1S_1 + c_2S_2 + \cdots + c_nS_n)$$
$$= (A - r_2I)(A - r_3I) \cdots (A - r_nI)c_1S_1$$
$$= (r_1 - r_2)(r_1 - r_3) \cdots (r_1 - r_n)c_1S_1 = 0,$$

if and only if $c_1 = 0$. Hence the columns S_j are linearly independent. Thus $AS = S \begin{bmatrix} r_1 & 0 & 0 & 0 \cdots 0 \\ 0 & r_2 & 0 & 0 \cdots 0 \\ 0 & 0 & r_3 & 0 \cdots 0 \\ \cdots\cdots\cdots\cdots\cdots \\ 0 & 0 & 0 & 0 \cdots r_n \end{bmatrix}$, and $S^{-1}AS$ has

the desired form.

Example.   Letting $A = \begin{bmatrix} 2 & -1 \\ -6 & 1 \end{bmatrix}$,   we   have $f(x) =$

$(x - 4)(x + 1)$, which has the two zeros 4 and -1. We solve the two systems of equation $AS_1 = 4S_1$ and $AS_2 = -S_2$. Thus we have $(A - 4I)S_1 = 0$ and $(A + I)S_2 = 0$, which, written out explicitly, are respectively

$$\begin{bmatrix} -2 & -1 \\ -6 & -3 \end{bmatrix}\begin{bmatrix} s_{11} \\ s_{21} \end{bmatrix} = 0 \quad \text{and} \quad \begin{bmatrix} 3 & -1 \\ -6 & 2 \end{bmatrix}\begin{bmatrix} s_{12} \\ s_{22} \end{bmatrix} = 0.$$

These equations give us $2s_{11} + s_{21} = 0$ and $3s_{12} - s_{22} = 0$. Choosing $s_{11} = 1$ and $s_{12} = 1$, we obtain $s_{21} = -2$ and $s_{22} = 3$. Thus $S = \begin{bmatrix} 1 & 1 \\ -2 & 3 \end{bmatrix}$ and $S^{-1}AS = \begin{bmatrix} 4 & 0 \\ 0 & -1 \end{bmatrix}$.

Exercises

Find nonsingular matrices S such that $S^{-1}AS$ is a matrix in diagonal form for each of the following matrices A:

1. $\begin{bmatrix} 2 & -1 \\ 2 & 5 \end{bmatrix}$.
2. $\begin{bmatrix} 2 & 5 \\ 4 & 1 \end{bmatrix}$.
3. $\begin{bmatrix} 1 & 0 \\ 2 & 3 \end{bmatrix}$

4. $\begin{bmatrix} 1 & 2 & 0 \\ 2 & 1 & 0 \\ 1 & 0 & -3 \end{bmatrix}$.
5. $\begin{bmatrix} 1 & 0 & -1 \\ 2 & 3 & 1 \\ 1 & 0 & 2 \end{bmatrix}$.
6. $\begin{bmatrix} 1 & 1 & -2 \\ 0 & 0 & 5 \\ 4 & 1 & 2 \end{bmatrix}$.

Groups, Rings, and Ideals

1 · Normal subgroups and factor groups

Now that we have another example of a noncommutative operation, namely the multiplication of matrices, we shall turn to a further study of the properties of groups. The student should review the definitions of a group, a subgroup, and the left and right cosets of a subgroup in a group.

Normal or invariant subgroup. Let S be a subgroup of a group G. Then, if $aS = Sa$ for every a in G, S is said to be a normal or invariant subgroup of G. Note that, if S is a normal subgroup of G, the right and left cosets of S in G coincide, so that we may speak of cosets without ambiguity.

Examples. Every subgroup of an abelian group is a normal subgroup. The subgroup $i = (1)(2)(3)$, (123), (132) is a normal subgroup of the symmetric group on three symbols. The right and left cosets of this subgroup in the symmetric group on three symbols are i, (123), (132) and (12), (13), (23), and hence $aS = Sa$ for every a in G.

Theorem 1. If S is a normal subgroup of a group G, then the product of two cosets of S in G is a coset of S in G.

By the product of two cosets $(aS)(bS)$ we mean the distinct elements obtained by multiplying every element of aS on the right by every element of bS. Now $(aS)(bS) = a(Sb)S = a(bS)S = (ab)(SS) = (ab)S$.

Theorem 2. If S is a normal subgroup of a group G, then the cosets of S in G form a group with respect to coset multiplication.

We have just proved that the product of two cosets of S is a coset of S. We can easily compute that $(aS)[(bS)(cS)] = [(aS)(bS)](cS)$. The identity element is S, for $S(aS) = (Sa)S = (aS)S = a(SS) = aS$, and the inverse of aS is $a^{-1}S$, for $(a^{-1}S)(aS) = (a^{-1}a)(SS) = iS = S$.

Example. The two cosets of the subgroup $i = (1)(2)(3)$, (123), (132) in the symmetric group on three symbols form a group of order 2.

Factor group. The group in Theorem 2 is called a factor group or a quotient group of the given group G. It is denoted by G/S. Only normal subgroups can be used to define a factor group of a group G. For, in order that the left cosets or the right cosets of a subgroup S in G form a group, we must demand either that the product of two left cosets of S in G is a left coset of S or that the product of two right cosets of S is a right coset of S. The following theorem shows that this condition implies that S is a normal subgroup.

Theorem 3.   If the product of two left cosets of a subgroup S in a group G is a left coset of S in G, then S is a normal subgroup.

Consider the product $S(aS)$. Since S contains the identity, it contains the left coset aS, and, since the product of two left cosets is a left coset, $S(aS) = aS$. But $S(aS) = (Sa)S$, and hence $S(aS)$ also contains the right coset Sa. Thus the right coset Sa is contained in the left coset aS. It remains to be proved that every element of aS is contained in Sa, for then $aS = Sa$. Let as_j be any element of aS, s_j being an element in S. Form the product $(as_j)(a^{-1}s_j^{-1}) = a(s_ja^{-1}s_j^{-1}) = a(a^{-1}s_k) = s_k$. Hence $as_j = s_k(s_ja) = s_va$, an element in Sa. Therefore every element of aS is contained in Sa, and $aS = Sa$ for every a in G.

Exercises

1. Prove that the following matrices form a group G with respect to matrix multiplication:

$$i = \begin{bmatrix} 1 & 0 \\ 0 & 1 \end{bmatrix}, \quad a = \begin{bmatrix} 0 & 1 \\ -1 & 0 \end{bmatrix}, \quad b = \begin{bmatrix} -1 & 0 \\ 0 & -1 \end{bmatrix}, \quad c = \begin{bmatrix} 0 & -1 \\ 1 & 0 \end{bmatrix},$$

$$d = \begin{bmatrix} 1 & 0 \\ 0 & -1 \end{bmatrix}, \quad e = \begin{bmatrix} 0 & 1 \\ 1 & 0 \end{bmatrix}, \quad f = \begin{bmatrix} -1 & 0 \\ 0 & 1 \end{bmatrix}, \quad g = \begin{bmatrix} 0 & -1 \\ -1 & 0 \end{bmatrix}.$$

2. In the following four exercises let G denote the group in Exercise 1.

    a) Prove that the subgroup S consisting of the elements i, b is a normal subgroup of G.

    b) Prove that the factor group G/S of G is not cyclic.

    c) Show that the elements i, a, b, c form a normal subgroup of G.

    d) Show that the elements i, d do not form a normal subgroup of G.

3. Let k denote the number of left cosets of a subgroup S in a group G. Prove that, if $k = 2$, the subgroup S is a normal subgroup.

4. Prove Theorem 3 for right cosets.

5. Prove: If G is an abelian group and S is a subgroup of G, then G/S is abelian.

2 · Conjugates

Definition. Let x and a be any elements of a group G. Then the element $x^{-1}ax$ is said to be conjugate to a under G, and $x^{-1}ax$ and a are called conjugate elements under G. The element $x^{-1}ax$ is also called the transform of the element a by x.

Theorem 4. *The elements of a group can be separated into mutually exclusive classes of conjugate elements.*

To prove this theorem we need merely show that the relation b conjugate to a under a group G is an equivalence relation. The three properties of an equivalence relation can be checked as follows. The element a is conjugate to a, for $i^{-1}ai = a$, where i is the identity. If a is conjugate to b, then b is conjugate to a, for if $a = x^{-1}bx$, then $b = xax^{-1} = (x^{-1})^{-1} ax^{-1}$. If a is conjugate to b, and if b is conjugate to c, then a is conjugate to c, for if $a = x^{-1}bx$ and $b = y^{-1}cy$, then $a = x^{-1}(y^{-1}cy)x = (yx)^{-1}c(yx)$. Thus the elements of a group can be separated into mutually exclusive classes of conjugate elements.

Example. The student can check that the elements of the symmetric group on three symbols can be separated into the following three classes of conjugate elements. The first class consists of the identity $i = (1)(2)(3)$; the second class consists of (123) and (132); and the third class consists of the elements (12), (13), and (23).

Theorem 5. *Those elements* x *of a group* G *such that* x^{-1}ax = a *form a subgroup* N *of* G, *called the normalizer of the element* a.

Note that this theorem says that all the elements of G which are commutative with a given element of G form a group. It is obvious that the normalizer contains the cyclic group generated by the given element. We proceed to the proof. Consider the set N of elements that are commutative with the element a. In order to prove that N is a subgroup, we need merely prove that the set N is closed and that if it contains x it contains x^{-1}. Let $x^{-1}ax = a$ and $y^{-1}ay = a$. Then $y^{-1}(x^{-1}ax)y = (xy)^{-1}a(xy) = a$. Thus the set N is closed. Now if x is in N it is obvious that x^{-1} is in N, for if $x^{-1}ax = a$, $a = xax^{-1} = (x^{-1})^{-1}ax^{-1}$.

Theorem 6.   Let N *be the normalizer of an element* a *of a group* G. *Then all the elements of the right coset* Nb *of* N *transform the element* a *into the same conjugate* $b^{-1}ab$. *Moreover, if* $b^{-1}ab = c^{-1}ac$, *then* Nb = Nc. *Thus there is a one-to-one correspondence between the right cosets of* N *in* G *and the elements conjugate to* a *under* G.

Any element n_ib of Nb transforms a into $b^{-1}ab$, for $(n_ib)^{-1}a(n_ib)$ $= b^{-1}(n_i^{-1}an_i)b = b^{-1}ab$. Now if $b^{-1}ab = c^{-1}ac$, then $(bc^{-1})^{-1}a(bc^{-1}) = a$ and bc^{-1} is in N. Thus $Nc = N(bc^{-1})c = Nb(c^{-1}c) = Nb$.

Corollary.   If G *is a finite group, the number of elements in a given class of conjugates is a divisor of the order of the group.*

By the previous theorem we need merely count the number of distinct right cosets of the normalizer of an element a in G to obtain the number of conjugates in a class. We previously proved that the number of right cosets of a subgroup in a group is a divisor of the order of the group.

Transform of a permutation.   It is of interest to find a simple way to transform any permutation by any other permutation. Let $a = (1\ 2\ 3 \cdots n)$ be any cycle of n symbols, and let $x = \begin{pmatrix} 1\ 2\ 3 \cdots n \\ i_1\ i_2\ i_3 \cdots i_n \end{pmatrix}$ be any permutation on these n symbols. Then $x^{-1} = \begin{pmatrix} i_1\ i_2\ i_3 \cdots i_n \\ 1\ 2\ 3 \cdots n \end{pmatrix}$, and it is easily seen that $x^{-1}ax = (i_1 i_2 i_3 \cdots i_n)$. Thus, to transform the permutation a by any other permutation, we replace the symbols in a by the symbols that follow them in the transforming permutation. Let $a = (123)(456)$ and $x = (2143)(56)$, for example. Then $x^{-1}ax = (412)(365)$.

Conjugate subgroups.   The relation of being conjugate is not restricted to the elements of a group. If x is an element of a group G and if S is a subgroup of G, then $x^{-1}Sx$ is a subgroup of G and is called a conjugate of S under G. It is easily seen that $x^{-1}Sx$, is a subgroup, for the product of two elements of the set $x^{-1}Sx$, $(x^{-1}s_ix)(x^{-1}s_jx) = x^{-1}(s_is_j)x$ is again an element of the set $x^{-1}Sx$. Moreover, if $x^{-1}s_ix$ is in $x^{-1}Sx$, then its inverse $x^{-1}s_i^{-1}x$ is in $x^{-1}Sx$. Thus it is easily seen that the word subgroup can be substituted for element throughout the preceding theorems on conjugate elements.

Note that our definition of a normal subgroup, i.e., a subgroup S of G such that $aS = Sa$ for every a in G, can be restated to read: S is a normal subgroup of G if $a^{-1}Sa = S$ for every a in G. We say, then, that a normal subgroup is *self-conjugate* under G.

Exercises

1. Separate the elements of the octic permutation group $i = (1)(2)(3)(4)$, (1234), $(13)(24)$, (1432), (13), (24), $(12)(34)$, $(14)(23)$ into classes of conjugate elements.

2. Find the normalizer of the element $(14)(23)$ in the octic group.

3. Find the normal subgroups of the octic group.

4. Find the classes of conjugate elements of the cyclic group of order 5.

3 · Automorphisms of a group

Definition. An isomorphism of a group with itself is an automorphism.

Theorem 7. The automorphisms of a group form a group.

Let $A_1 : a \leftrightarrow a'$ and $A_2 : a \leftrightarrow a''$ be two automorphisms of a group G, a, a', and a'' denoting the elements of the group G. Now we may write A_2 as $a' \leftrightarrow (a')''$, for the order in which we write the elements of G is immaterial. Thus we may set up the one-to-one correspondence $a \leftrightarrow (a')''$ between the elements of G. This correspondence is an automorphism of G called the product A_1A_2 of the automorphisms A_1 and A_2 of G, for we have $[(ab)']'' = (a'b')'' = (a')''(b')''$. Thus the product of two automorphisms of a group is an automorphism of the group. The correspondence $a \leftrightarrow a$ in which each element of G corresponds to itself is the identity element of the automorphism group. Now if $A_1 : a \leftrightarrow a'$ is an automorphism of G, then $a' \leftrightarrow a$ is an automorphism of G which is the inverse A_1^{-1} of A_1, for $A_1A_1^{-1}$ is the correspondence $a \leftrightarrow a$. The associative law holds, for, if A_1 and A_2 are the above automorphisms and if A_3 is the automorphism $a \leftrightarrow a'''$, we may write

A_2 as $a' \leftrightarrow (a')''$ and A_3 as $a'' \leftrightarrow (a'')'''$. Hence $(A_1A_2)A_3$ is the automorphism $a \leftrightarrow [(a')'']'''$, while A_2A_3 is the automorphism $a' \leftrightarrow [(a')'']'''$ and $A_1(A_2A_3)$ is therefore the automorphism $a \leftrightarrow [(a')'']'''$. Thus the postulates for a group are satisfied.

Theorem 8. For any fixed element x *of a group* G, *the correspondence* a $\leftrightarrow$ x^{-1}ax *is an automorphism of* G.

If $a \leftrightarrow x^{-1}ax$ and if $b \leftrightarrow x^{-1}bx$, then $ab \leftrightarrow (x^{-1}ax)(x^{-1}bx) = x^{-1}(ab)x$.

Automorphisms that may be established by transforming the elements of a group G by a fixed element x of G are called *inner* automorphisms of G. All other automorphisms are called *outer* automorphisms of G.

Theorem 9. The inner automorphisms of a group G *form a normal subgroup* I *of the group* A *of automorphisms of* G.

Let $a \leftrightarrow x^{-1}ax$ and $a \leftrightarrow y^{-1}ay$ be two inner automorphisms of G. Their product is $a \leftrightarrow y^{-1}(x^{-1}ax)y = (xy)^{-1}a(xy)$, which is an inner automorphism of G. The identity element of the group of automorphisms is an inner automorphism, for $a \leftrightarrow i^{-1}ai = a$. The inverse of the inner automorphism $a \leftrightarrow x^{-1}ax$ is $a \leftrightarrow xax^{-1}$, for their product is $a \leftrightarrow x(x^{-1}ax)x^{-1} = a$. Thus the inner automorphisms form a subgroup I of the group A of automorphisms of G.

It remains to be proved that I is a normal subgroup of A. Let $a \leftrightarrow a'$ be any automorphism A_1 of G, and let $a \leftrightarrow x^{-1}ax$ be an inner automorphism I_1 of G. We show that $A_1^{-1}I_1A_1$ is again an inner automorphism of G. Now A_1^{-1} is $a' \leftrightarrow a$, and hence $A_1^{-1}I_1$ is $a' \leftrightarrow x^{-1}ax$. Note that A_1 gives $x^{-1}ax \leftrightarrow (x')^{-1}a'x'$. Thus $(A_1^{-1}I_1)A_1$ is $a' \leftrightarrow (x')^{-1}a'x'$, which is an inner automorphism of G.

Examples.

1. The cyclic group of order four a, a^2, a^3, $a^4 = i$ has no inner automorphism except the identity, but it has the following outer automorphism:

$$i \leftrightarrow i$$
$$a \leftrightarrow a^3$$
$$a^2 \leftrightarrow a^2$$
$$a^3 \leftrightarrow a.$$

Thus the group of automorphisms is of order 2.

2. The group of automorphisms of the symmetric group on three symbols consists of inner automorphisms. The symmetric group on three symbols has no outer automorphisms. We list the automorphisms, and under each automorphism we give the transforming permutation x used to establish the automorphism:

$i \leftrightarrow i$	$i \leftrightarrow i$	$i \leftrightarrow i$
$(123) \leftrightarrow (123)$	$(123) \leftrightarrow (132)$	$(123) \leftrightarrow (132)$
$(132) \leftrightarrow (132)$	$(132) \leftrightarrow (123)$	$(132) \leftrightarrow (123)$
$(12) \leftrightarrow (12)$	$(12) \leftrightarrow (13)$	$(12) \leftrightarrow (12)$
$(13) \leftrightarrow (13)$	$(13) \leftrightarrow (12)$	$(13) \leftrightarrow (23)$
$(23) \leftrightarrow (23)$	$(23) \leftrightarrow (23)$	$(23) \leftrightarrow (13)$
$x = i$	$x = (23)$	$x = (12)$

$i \leftrightarrow i$	$i \leftrightarrow i$	$i \leftrightarrow i$
$(123) \leftrightarrow (132)$	$(123) \leftrightarrow (123)$	$(123) \leftrightarrow (123)$
$(132) \leftrightarrow (123)$	$(132) \leftrightarrow (132)$	$(132) \leftrightarrow (132)$
$(12) \leftrightarrow (23)$	$(12) \leftrightarrow (23)$	$(12) \leftrightarrow (13)$
$(13) \leftrightarrow (13)$	$(13) \leftrightarrow (12)$	$(13) \leftrightarrow (23)$
$(23) \leftrightarrow (12)$	$(23) \leftrightarrow (13)$	$(23) \leftrightarrow (12)$
$x = (13)$	$x = (123)$	$x = (132)$

Exercises

1. Find the order of each of the automorphisms of the symmetric group on three symbols.

2. Find the group of automorphisms of the group of the five fifth roots of unity. Is it cyclic? Are any of these automorphisms inner automorphisms?

3. Find the group of automorphisms of the octic group.

4. Find the group of automorphisms of the cyclic group of order 6.

5. Find the group of automorphisms of the four group $i = (1)(2)(3)(4)$, $(12)(34)$, $(13)(24)$, $(14)(23)$.

6. Find the group of automorphisms of the alternating group on four symbols. Are any of the automorphisms outer automorphisms?

4 · Homomorphisms of groups

Definition. Let a, b, c, $\cdots$ denote the elements of a group G, and let a', b', c', $\cdots$ denote the elements of a group G'. The group G' is said to be a homomorphic image of the group G if a correspondence $a \rightarrow a'$ can be set up from the elements of G

onto the elements of G' such that

1) every element a in G has exactly one image a' in G',
2) every element of G' occurs at least once as an image,
3) if $a \to a'$ and $b \to b'$, then $ab \to a'b'$.

The correspondence is called a homomorphism of G onto G'.

Note the omission of the double arrow to indicate that the mapping is from G onto G'. A homomorphism is not in general a one-to-one correspondence but a many-to-one correspondence. If the correspondence is one-to-one, a homomorphism reduces to an isomorphism.

Example. Let G be the symmetric group on n symbols, and let G' be the multiplicative group of order 2 consisting of the elements 1 and -1. A homomorphism can be set up by letting every even permutation have the image 1 and every odd permutation the image -1.

Theorem 10. *Let a group* G' *be the homomorphic image of a group* G. *Then the image of the identity in* G *is the identity in* G', *and, if* $a \to a'$, *then* $a^{-1} \to (a')^{-1}$.

This theorem is proved in the same way in which we proved the corresponding theorem for an isomorphism between two groups. Let the identity i of G have the image a' in the homomorphism, and let x' be any element of G'. Let x be an element of G which has x' as its image in G'. Then $ix \to a'x'$. However, $ix = x$, and so $a'x' = x'$ for any element x' of G. Hence a' is the identity of G'. Similarly, let $x^{-1} \to b'$, then $x^{-1}x \to b'x'$. However, $x^{-1}x = i$, and so $b'x' = i'$, the identity of G'. Thus b' is the inverse of x'.

Now put into one class all those elements a of G which have the same image a' in G'. The following theorem describes these classes.

Theorem 11. *Let a group* G' *be a homomorphic image of a group* G. *Then those elements* a *of* G *whose image is the identity in* G' *form a normal subgroup* S *of* G, *and those elements of* G *which have the same image in* G' *form a coset of* S *in* G. *The factor group* G/S *is isomorphic to* G'.

Consider the elements in G which have the identity i' as an image in G'. Denote this set by S. If $a \to i'$ and $b \to i'$, then $ab \to i'i' = i'$. Thus the set S is closed. Further, if $a \to i'$, then by the previous theorem $a^{-1} \rightarrow (i')^{-1} = i'$, and so the inverse of each element in S is in S. Hence S is a subgroup of G.

We next prove that S is a normal subgroup of G. Now all the elements of the left coset xS have the same image in G', for, if $x \rightarrow x'$, then $xS \rightarrow x'i' = x'$. Moreover, if $y \rightarrow x'$, then as we shall prove, y lies in xS. Now $x^{-1}y \rightarrow (x')^{-1}x' = i'$. Hence $x^{-1}y$ is in S and y is in xS. Similarly we can prove that all the elements of G whose image is x' in G' form the right coset Sx. Hence $Sx = xS$ and S is a normal subgroup of G.

Note that we have established a one-to-one correspondence between the cosets of S in G and the elements a' of G'. Hence if $aS \rightarrow a'$ and $bS \rightarrow b'$, then $(aS)(bS) = (ab)S \rightarrow a'b'$. Hence the factor group G/S and G' are isomorphic.

Definition. The subgroup S is called the kernel of the homomorphism.

Now combining our previous discussion of a factor group of G with the definition of homomorphism, we have the following theorem.

Theorem 12. Let S be a normal subgroup of a group G. Then the factor group G/S is a homomorphic image of G.

Example. We may set up a homomorphism of the alternating group on four symbols onto the cyclic group of order 3 as follows:

$$
\begin{aligned}
i = (1)(2)(3)(4) &\rightarrow & i' = a^3 \\
(12)(34) &\rightarrow & i' \\
(13)(24) &\rightarrow & i' \\
(14)(23) &\rightarrow & i' \\
(123) &\rightarrow & a \\
(243) &\rightarrow & a \\
(142) &\rightarrow & a \\
(134) &\rightarrow & a \\
(132) &\rightarrow & a^2 \\
(143) &\rightarrow & a^2 \\
(234) &\rightarrow & a^2 \\
(124) &\rightarrow & a^2.
\end{aligned}
$$

Exercises

1. Set up a homomorphism of the octic group onto the cyclic group of order 2.

2. Set up a homomorphism of the octic group onto the permutation group
$i = (1)(2)(3)(4), (12)(34), (13)(24), (14)(23)$.

3. Set up a homomorphism of the cyclic group of order 8 onto the cyclic group of order 4.

4. Set up a homomorphism of the symmetric group on four symbols onto the symmetric group on three symbols.

5. Set up a homomorphism of the additive group of integers onto the additive group of residue classes modulo 3.

6. Set up a homomorphism of the additive group of integers onto the additive group of residue classes modulo m.

5 · Ideals in commutative rings

We shall now apply the theory of factor groups and homomorphisms of groups to commutative rings. In order to do this we must define a new concept, namely, that of an ideal in a commutative ring. An ideal in a ring is a certain kind of subring which plays a role analogous to that played by a normal subgroup in a group. Hence we first need necessary and sufficient conditions that a nonempty subset S of elements of a ring R be a subring. These are:

1) the elements of S form an additive subgroup of the additive group of R;

2) the set S is closed with respect to multiplication; i.e., if a and b are in S, then ab is in S.

Condition 1) is often phrased as follows: if a and b are in S, then $a - b$ is in S. The student should check that this is a necessary and sufficient condition that a nonempty subset of an additive group be a subgroup. We shall use this formulation of condition 1) in our definition of an ideal in a commutative ring. It is customary to denote ideals by German letters.

Definition of an ideal. A nonempty subset of elements $\mathfrak{m}$ of a commutative ring R is an ideal if the following two conditions are satisfied:

1) if a and b are in $\mathfrak{m}$, then $a - b$ is in $\mathfrak{m}$;

2) if a is in $\mathfrak{m}$ and if r is in R, then ra is in $\mathfrak{m}$.

Examples.

1. The even integers form an ideal in the ring of integers, for, if $2n$ and $2m$ are in the ideal, then $2n - 2m = 2(n - m)$ is in the ideal. Moreover, if r is any integer, then $r(2n) = 2(rn)$ is an even integer.

Isomorphism
Def. of

Cyclic groups
Def. of

Def. of order of an element

Def. of order of a group

Th-m 12

If a generator of a cyclic group Grp of
order zero, Grp isomorphic to the additive
group of integers. If a generator a of a

Groups

Def. 5

1. The n-n th roots of unity form a group with respect to multiplication.

2. The residue classes mod m form a group with respect to addition.

3. The non-zero residue classes mod P form a gp. with respect to multiplication if and only if P is a prime.

4. The residue classes $C_a \ni (a,m)=1$ form a group with respect to multiplication

Th$\underline{^{m}}$ 1. If a, b, c are in a group, $ab = ac \Rightarrow b = c$

$ba = ca \Rightarrow b = c$

Th$\underline{^{m}}$ 4. If a and b are elements in a group, the equations $ax = b$ and $ya = b$, respectively, group.

Cor. 1. The identity element in a group is unique.

Cor. 2. The inverse of an element in a group is unique.

Cor. 3 The inverse of a^{-1} is a

Thm 5. The inverse of a product is a product of the inverses.

The additive group of
modulo n.

Subgroups
proper subgrps..?

Thm 13. Necessary and sufficient conditions
that a subset S of elements of a group
G forms a group are 1) if a and b are in
S, then $a \cdot b$ is in S, and 2) if a is in S, then
a^{-1} is in S.

2. The ring R itself is an ideal called the unit ideal of the ring.

3. The zero element of a ring is an ideal in the ring called the zero ideal. It is denoted by (0).

4. Let $R[x]$ be the ring of polynomials with integral coefficients. The polynomials of degree zero (i.e., the integers) together with the zero polynomial form a subring of $R[x]$. However, this subring is not an ideal, for, if $f(x)$ is any polynomial in $R[x]$ of degree greater than zero, and if a is any integer, $af(x)$ is not an integer.

5. The ideal generated by an element a of a ring R consists of all elements of the form $ra + na$, where r is in R and n is an integer. This ideal is called a *principal* ideal and is denoted by (a). We prove that the set of elements of the given form $ra + na$ form an ideal. First, if $r_1a + n_1a$ and $r_2a + n_2a$ are in the set, then $r_1a + n_1a - (r_2a + n_2a) = (r_1 - r_2)a + (n_1 - n_2)a$ is of the given form. Next let r be any element of R. Then $r(r_1a + n_1a) = (rr_1 + rn_1)a = r'a + 0 \cdot a$, where r' is in R. Note that, when R has a unity element u, every element of the principal ideal (a) can be written as ra, where r is an element of R. For an element $r'a + na$, where n is an integer, can be written as $r'a + n(ua) = r'a + (nu)a = ra$ when nu is an element of R.

6. Similarly, we define the ideal $(a_1, a_2, \cdots, a_n)$ in a ring R generated by the finite number of elements $a_1, a_2, \cdots, a_n$ of R as the set of elements of the form $\sum_{i=1}^{n} r_ia_i + \sum_{j=1}^{n} n_ja_j$, where the r_i are in R and the n_j are integers. The elements $a_1, a_2, \cdots, a_n$ are said to form a *basis* of the ideal.

Exercises

1. Prove that the integral multiples of any fixed integer m in the ring of integers form an ideal.

2. In the ring of integers prove that the ideal $(6, 4) = (2)$.

3. In the ring of integers prove that the ideal $(9, 25)$ is the ring of integers.

4. In the ring of polynomials $R[x]$, where R is the ring of integers, prove that all polynomials whose constant term is zero form an ideal. Is this a principal ideal? If so, what is its generator?

5. Using the fact that every subgroup of a cyclic group is cyclic, prove that every ideal in the ring of integers is a principal ideal.

6. Prove that the only ideals in the field of rational numbers are the zero ideal (0) and the field itself.

7. Prove that the only ideals in any field are the zero ideal and the field itself.

8. Find all the ideals in the ring of residue classes modulo 10.

9. Show that in the polynomial ring $R[x]$, where R is the field of rational numbers, the ideal $(x^2 + 5x + 6, x + 3) = (x + 3)$.

10. Show that every ideal in the polynomial ring $F[x]$, where F is a field, is a principal ideal. Hint: Show that the ideal either consists of the zero ideal or contains a polynomial $r(x)$ of least degree such that every polynomial in the ideal is a polynomial times $r(x)$.

6 · Residue class rings

Ideals enable us to construct rings from a given ring in the same way we constructed factor groups by means of normal subgroups. Since an ideal $\mathfrak{m}$ in a commutative ring R is a normal subgroup of the additive group of the ring, the elements of the ring can be separated into cosets of $\mathfrak{m}$ in R. These cosets are called residue classes of R modulo the ideal $\mathfrak{m}$. Thus a residue class modulo $\mathfrak{m}$ is the set of elements $\mathfrak{m} + a$, where a is any element of the ring R. Recall that a necessary and sufficient condition for the equality of two cosets Sa and Sb of a subgroup S in a group G is that ab^{-1} be in S. (See p. 55, Exercise 6.) This condition translated into the additive notation and applied as a criterion for the equality of two residue classes $\mathfrak{m} + a$ and $\mathfrak{m} + b$ is that $a - b$ be in the ideal $\mathfrak{m}$. We now define $a \equiv b$ (mod $\mathfrak{m}$) if and only if $a - b$ is in $\mathfrak{m}$. Thus we have a generalization of the idea of congruences of integers. We prove the following rules governing congruences modulo an ideal $\mathfrak{m}$.

Theorem 13. Let R *be a commutative ring and* $\mathfrak{m}$ *an ideal in* R. *If* $a \equiv b$ *(mod* $\mathfrak{m}$) *and if* $a' \equiv b'$ *(mod* $\mathfrak{m}$), *then* $a + a' \equiv b + b'$ *(mod* $\mathfrak{m}$), $aa' \equiv bb'$ *(mod* $\mathfrak{m}$), *and* $ra \equiv rb$ *(mod* $\mathfrak{m}$), *where* r *is in* R.

Since $a - b$ and $a' - b'$ are both in $\mathfrak{m}$, then $(a - b) + (a' - b')$ $= (a + a') - (b + b')$ is in $\mathfrak{m}$, and $a + a' \equiv b + b'$ (mod $\mathfrak{m}$). Further, since $a - b$ is in $\mathfrak{m}$, $a'(a - b)$ is in $\mathfrak{m}$, and since $a' - b'$ is in $\mathfrak{m}$, $(a' - b')b$ is in $\mathfrak{m}$. Therefore $a'(a - b) + (a' - b')b = a'a - b'b$ is in $\mathfrak{m}$, and $a'a \equiv b'b$ (mod $\mathfrak{m}$). Obviously, if $a - b$ is in $\mathfrak{m}$, $r(a - b)$ is in $\mathfrak{m}$, and $ra \equiv rb$ (mod $\mathfrak{m}$).

Definition of addition and multiplication of residue classes. Let a be an element of the residue class $\mathfrak{m} + a$ and let b be an element of the residue class $\mathfrak{m} + b$. The sum of the two residue classes $\mathfrak{m} + a$ and $\mathfrak{m} + b$ is defined as the class containing the element $a + b$. The product of the two residue classes $\mathfrak{m} + a$ and $\mathfrak{m} + b$ is defined as the residue class containing the product ab. Note that by the previous theorem the sum residue class and the product residue class are independent of the particular representatives chosen from the given residue classes.

Theorem 14. Let R *be a commutative ring and* m *an ideal in* R. *The residue classes modulo* m *form a ring with respect to addition and multiplication.*

The ring formed by the residue classes modulo m is called a *residue class ring* and is denoted by R/m.

From the theory of groups we know that the residue classes form an additive abelian group, for they are the cosets of a normal subgroup m in an additive abelian group R. The above definition of product of two residue classes gives us the closure with respect to multiplication. It is left to the student to prove the associative laws for multiplication and the distributive law.

Examples.

1. Let R be the ring of integers and let $m = (m)$. Then $R/(m)$ is the ring of residue classes modulo the integer m.

2. Let $R[x]$ be the polynomial ring, where R is the ring of integers and m the ideal $(x - 3)$. The ideal $(x - 3)$ consists of all elements of the form $f(x)(x - 3)$, where $f(x)$ is a polynomial in $R[x]$. Now any polynomial $g(x)$ in $R[x]$ can be written as $g(x) = q(x)(x - 3) + g(3)$. Therefore $g(x) \equiv g(3) \pmod{(x - 3)}$. That is to say, any residue class can be represented by an integer. Now if two integers a and b lie in the same residue class, $a - b$ is in the ideal $(x - 3)$; that is, $a - b = q(x)(x - 3)$. Now unless $q(x) = 0$, the degree of the right-hand side is greater than zero. Hence $q(x) = 0$ and $a = b$. Thus every integer determines a different residue class. Hence we can set up a one-to-one correspondence between the residue classes of $R[x]$ modulo $(x - 3)$ and the integers a by letting $(x - 3) + a \leftrightarrow a$. The student can easily check that this correspondence is an isomorphism.

3. Let R be the ring of complex numbers $a + bi$, where a and b are integers, and let $m = (2)$. Then, since 2 and $2i$ are elements of m, any number $a + bi = 2k + r + (2k' + r')i$, where $0 \leq r < 2$ and $0 \leq r' < 2$. Thus $a + bi \equiv r + r'i \pmod{(2)}$. Hence we have the four distinct residue classes: (2), $(2) + 1$, $(2) + i$, $(2) + 1 + i$.

Exercises

1. Determine whether the residue classes in Example 3 form an integral domain.

2. Exhibit the residue class ring of the ring of complex numbers of the form $a + bi$, where a and b are integers, modulo the ideal (3). Is this residue class ring a field?

3. Exhibit the residue class ring of the ring $R[x]$, where R is the ring of integers, modulo the ideal (x).

4. Exhibit the residue class ring of the ring $R[x]$, where R is the ring of integers, modulo the ideal $(x^2 + 1)$.

7 · Homomorphisms of rings

The definition of a homomorphism of a ring is an extension of the definition of a homomorphism of a group. The correspondence merely preserves two operations instead of one.

Definition. Let a, b, c, $\cdots$ denote the elements of a ring R, and let a', b', c', $\cdots$ denote the elements of a ring R'. The ring R' is said to be a homomorphic image of the ring R if a correspondence $a \rightarrow a'$ can be set up from the elements of R onto the elements of R' such that

1) every element a in R has exactly one image a' in R',
2) every element of R' occurs at least once as an image,
3) if $a \rightarrow a'$ and $b \rightarrow b'$, then $a + b \rightarrow a' + b'$ and $ab \rightarrow a'b'$.

Again we note that a homomorphism is a many-to-one mapping of the elements of R onto the elements of R'. We show the intimate relation between ideals and the homomorphism of rings in the following theorem.

Theorem 15. If a ring R' is a homomorphic image of a commutative ring R, those elements of R whose image is the zero element of R' form an ideal $\mathfrak{m}$, and the residue class ring $\mathrm{R}/\mathfrak{m}$ is isomorphic to R'.

We first show that those elements of R whose image is the zero element of R' form an ideal $\mathfrak{m}$. Denote the zero element of R' by $0'$. Then, if $a \rightarrow 0'$ and $b \rightarrow 0'$, we have $a - b \rightarrow 0' - 0' = 0'$. Further, if r is any element of the ring R whose image is r' in R', $ra \rightarrow r' \cdot 0' = 0'$. Thus those elements of R whose image is the zero element of R' form an ideal $\mathfrak{m}$ in R. Now separate the elements of R into residue classes modulo $\mathfrak{m}$. If $a \rightarrow a'$, all the elements of the residue class $\mathfrak{m} + a$ have the image a', for any element $m + a$, where m is in $\mathfrak{m}$, of this class is mapped onto $0' + a' = a'$. Moreover, if $b \to a'$, then $a - b \to a' - a' = 0'$, and $a - b$ is in $\mathfrak{m}$. If now we regard the residue classes of R modulo $\mathfrak{m}$ as elements, the correspondence $\mathfrak{m} + a \to a'$ is obviously an isomorphism, for if $\mathfrak{m} + b \to b'$, then $\mathfrak{m} + a + b \to a' + b'$, and $\mathfrak{m} + ab \to a'b'$.

Now, combining our previous discussion of residue class rings of a ring R with our definition of homomorphism, we can see that any residue class ring of R is a homomorphic image of R. Let $\mathfrak{m}$ be an ideal in R, then the correspondence $a \to \mathfrak{m} + a$ gives us the homomorphism. Hence we have the following theorem.

Theorem 16. Every ideal $\mathfrak{m}$ in a commutative ring R determines a homomorphism of R onto its residue class ring $R/\mathfrak{m}$.

Exercises

1. Prove that a homomorphic image of a commutative ring is a commutative ring.

2. Prove that, if R' is a homomorphic image of a ring R with unity element, R' has a unity element.

3. What are the possible homomorphic images of a field?

4. The polynomial ring $F[x]$, where F is the field of rational numbers, is mapped homomorphically onto the ring of complex numbers $a + bi$, where a and b are rational, by the correspondence $f(x) \to f(i)$. What is the ideal that determines the homomorphism?

5. Find all the ideals in the residue class ring of integers modulo 12. Hence find all the homomorphic images of this residue class ring.

Bibliography

Aitken, A. C., *Determinants and Matrices*, Oliver and Boyd, Edinburgh, 1939.

Albert, A. A., *College Algebra*, McGraw-Hill Book Co., New York, 1946.

Albert, A. A., *Introduction to Algebraic Theories*, University of Chicago Press, 1941.

Albert, A. A., *Modern Higher Algebra*, University of Chicago Press, 1937.

Birkhoff, G., and MacLane, S., *A Survey of Modern Algebra*, The Macmillan Co., New York, 1941.

Burnside, W., *Theory of Groups of Finite Order*, 2nd edition, Cambridge University Press, London, 1911.

Carmichael, R. D., *Introduction to the Theory of Groups of Finite Order*, Ginn and Co., Boston, 1937.

Dickson, L. E., *Modern Elementary Theory of Numbers*, University of Chicago Press, 1939.

Dickson, L. E., *New First Course in the Theory of Equations*, John Wiley & Sons, New York, 1939.

Dubreil, Paul, *Algèbre*, Vol. 1, Gauthier-Villars, Paris, 1946.

Frazier, R. A., Duncan, W. J., and Collar, A. R., *Elementary Matrices and Some Applications to Dynamics and Differential Equations*, Cambridge University Press, London, 1938.

Griffiths, L. W., *Introduction to the Theory of Equations*, John Wiley & Sons, New York, 1947.

Hardy, G. H., and Wright, E. M., *An Introduction to the Theory of Numbers*, Oxford, 1938.

Hasse, H., *Höhere Algebra*, Vols. 1 and 2, 2nd edition, Walter de Gruyter and Co. (Sammlung Göschen), Leipzig, 1933.

Hecke, E., *Vorlesüngen über die Theorie der algebraischen Zahlen*, Akademische Verlagsgesellschaft M.B.H., Leipzig, 1923.

Landau, E., *Grundlagen der Analysis*, Akademische Verlagsgesellschaft M.B.H., Leipzig, 1930.

Landau, E., *Vorlesungen über Zahlentheorie*, Vol. 1, Hirzel, Leipzig, 1927.

MacDuffee, C. C., *An Introduction to Abstract Algebra*, John Wiley & Sons, New York, 1940.

MacDuffee, C. C., *Vectors and Matrices*, Carus Mathematical Monograph, No. 7, The Mathematical Association of America, 1943.

Miller, G. A., Blichfeldt, H. F., and Dickson, L. E., *Theory and Applications of Finite Groups*, John Wiley & Sons, New York, 1916.

Pontrjagin, L., *Topological Groups*, Princeton University Press, 1939.

Speiser, A., *Theorie der Gruppen von endlicher Ordnung*, 3rd edition, Springer, Berlin, 1937.

Thomas, J. M., *Theory of Equations*, McGraw-Hill Book Co., New York, 1938.

Uspensky, J. V., and Heaslet, M. A., *Elementary Number Theory*, McGraw-Hill Book Co., New York, 1939.

van der Waerden, B. L., *Moderne Algebra*, Vols. 1 and 2, 2nd edition, Springer, Berlin, 1937 and 1940.

Weisner, L., *Theory of Equations*, The Macmillan Co., New York, 1938.

Wright, H. N., *First Course in the Theory of Numbers*, John Wiley & Sons, New York, 1939.

Zassenhaus, H., *Lehrbuch der Gruppentheorie*, Teubner, Leipzig, 1937.

INDEX